The Way Home

Harry Mathews

THE WAY HOME

Selected Longer Prose

ATLAS PRESS

1999

The Way Home is published by

Atlas Press, 27 Old Gloucester St., London WC1N 3XX.

©1989 & 1999, Harry Mathews.

This edition ©1999, Atlas Press.

All rights reserved.

Armenian Papers ©1987 Harry Mathews,

reprinted by permission of Princeton University Press.

Cover photograph of the author by Arthur Gerbault.

Printed by The Guernsey Press, Channel Islands.

A CIP record for this book is available from the British Library.

ISBN I 900565 05 6

Contents

Preface

This second edition of *The Way Home* differs significantly from the first. Thanks to the recent republication of *Selected Declarations of Dependence* by Sun & Moon Press, "Their Words, For You" has reappeared in its proper role as the opening section of that book; it has therefore been withdrawn from this one. Its place has been filled by two works, "Armenian Papers" and "Translation and the Oulipo: The Case of the Persevering Maltese". In addition, Trevor Winkfield's drawings, which provided a starting point for the title story of this collection, are now incorporated into the text as they were on its first publication.

The seven pieces now included were written over a period of sixteen years. Four of them were prompted into existence by the requests of others. "Country Cooking" (1977) was a response to the invitation of an editor planning a travel issue of his review. "The Way Home" (1988) originated in Trevor Winkfield's suggestion that we do a work in collaboration. "Autobiography" (1988) was solicited for an annual series devoted to contemporary American authors. "Translation and the Oulipo: The Case of the Persevering Maltese" was commissioned as the third St. Jerome lecture.

Of the other works, "Armenian Papers" (ca. 1980-1985), originally composed in verse, began as an attempt to write a poem a day, without any preconceived shape or subject. The exercise was sustained for about ten days; by then the unexpected exotic continuity of the poems had been established, to be completed in fits and starts during the following years. Somewhat similarly,

7

"Singular Pleasures" emerged without warning when six of its episodes sprang full-blown into being at four o'clock on a March morning in 1981; the remainder followed within a week or two. As for "The Orchard" (1982), the foreword attached to it describes its distressing genesis. (Appended to the piece are notes that explain various references and translate its snatches of French.)

Earnest thanks are due to the following publishers for permission to republish works still in print: the Grenfell Press for "The Way Home"; the Grenfell Press and Dalkey Archive Press for "Singular Pleasures"; Princeton University Press and Carcanet Press for "Armenian Papers"; Gale Research Company for "Autobiography"; and Bamberger Books for "The Orchard".

COUNTRY COOKING
FROM CENTRAL FRANCE:
ROAST BONED ROLLED STUFFED
SHOULDER OF LAMB
(*FARCE DOUBLE*)

for Maxine Groffsky

Here is an old French regional dish for you to try. Attempts by presumptuous chefs to refine it have failed to subdue its basically hearty nature. It demands some patience, but you will be abundantly rewarded for your pains.

Farce double — literally, double stuffing — is the speciality of La Tour Lambert, a mountain village in Auvergne, that rugged heart of the Massif Central. I have often visited La Tour Lambert: the first time was in late May, when *farce double* is traditionally served. I have observed the dish being made and discussed it with local cooks.

The latter were sceptical about reproducing *farce double* elsewhere — not out of pride, but because they were afraid the dish would make no sense to a foreigner. (It is your duty to prove them wrong — and nothing would make them happier if you did.) Furthermore, they said, certain ingredients would be hard to find. Judicious substitution is our answer to that. Without it, after all, we would have to forgo most foreign cooking not out of a can.

The shoulder of lamb itself requires attention. You must buy it from a butcher who can dress it properly. Tell him to include the middle neck, the shoulder chops in the brisket, and part of the foreshank. The stuffing will otherwise fall out of the roast.

In Auvergne, preparing the cut is no problem, since whole lambs are roasted: the dish is considered appropriate for exceptional, often communal feasts, of a kind that has become a rarity with us.

All bones must be removed. If you leave this to the butcher, have him save them for the deglazing sauce. The fell or filament must be kept intact, or the flesh may crumble.

Set the boned forequarter on the kitchen table. Do not slice off the purple inspection stamps but scour them with a brush dipped in a weak solution of lye. The meat will need all the protection it can get. Rinse and dry.

Marinate the lamb in a mixture of 2 qts of white wine, 2 qts of olive oil, the juice of 16 lemons, salt, pepper, 16 crushed garlic cloves, 10 coarsely chopped yellow onions, basil, rosemary, melilot, ginger, allspice, and a handful of juniper berries. The juniper adds a pungent, authentic note. In Auvergne, shepherds pick the berries in late summer when they drive their flocks from the mountain pastures. They deposit the berries in La Tour Lambert, where they are pickled through the winter in cider brandy. The preparation is worth making, but demands foresight.

If no bowl is capacious enough for the lamb and its marinade, use a wash-tub. Without a tub, you must improvise. Friends of mine in Paris resort to their bidet; Americans may have to fall back on the kitchen sink, which is what I did the first time I made *farce double*. In La Tour Lambert, most houses have stone marinating troughs. Less favoured citizens use the municipal troughs in the entrance of a cave in the hillside, just off the main square.

The lamb will have marinated satisfactorily in 5 or 6 days.

Allow yourself 3 hours for the stuffings. The fish balls or quenelles that are their main ingredient can be prepared a day in advance and refrigerated until an hour before use.

The quenelles of La Tour Lambert have traditionally been made from *chaste*, a fish peculiar to the mountain lakes of Auvergne. The name, a dialect word meaning "fresh blood", may have been suggested by the colour of its spreading gills, through which it ingests its food. (It is a mouthless fish.) It is lured to the surface with a skein of tiny beads that resemble the larvae on which it preys, then bludgeoned with an underwater boomerang. *Chaste* has coarse, yellow-white flesh, with a mild but inescapable taste. It has been vaguely and mistakenly identified as a perch; our American perch, however, can replace it, provided it has been caught no more than 36 hours before cooking. Other substitutes are saltwater fish such as silver hake or green cod. If you use a dry-fleshed fish, remember to order beef-kidney fat at the butcher's to add to the fish paste. (Be sure to grind it separately.)

To a saucepan filled with 2½ cups of cold water, add salt, pepper, 2 pinches of grated nutmeg, and 6 tbsp of butter. Boil. Off heat, begin stirring in 2½ cups of flour and continue as you again bring the water to a boil. Take off heat. Beat in 5 eggs, one at a time, then 5 egg whites. Let the liquid cool.

Earlier, you will have ground 3¾ lbs of fish with a mortar and pestle — heads, tails, bones, and all — and forced them through a coarse sieve. Do *not* use a grinder, blender, or Cuisinart. The sieve of La Tour Lambert is an elegant sock of meshed copper wire, with a fitted ashwood plunger. It is kept immaculately bright. Its apertures are shrewdly gauged to mince the bones without pulverising the fish. Into the strained fish, mix small amounts of salt, white pepper, nutmeg, and chopped truffles — fresh ones, if possible. (See TRUFFLE.)

Stir fish and liquid into an even paste.

Two hours before, you will have refrigerated 1 cup of the heaviest cream available. Here, of course, access to a cow is a blessing.

The breathtaking viscid cream of La Tour Lambert is kept in specially excavated cellars. Those without one use the town chiller, in the middle depths — cool but not cold — of the cave mentioned earlier. Often I have watched the attendant women entering and emerging from that room, dusky figures in cowls, shawls, and long grey gowns, bearing earthenware jugs like offerings to a saint.

Beat the cool cream into the paste. Do it slowly: think of those erect, deliberate Auvergnat women as they stand in the faint gloom of the cave, beating with gestures of timeless calm. It should take at least 15 minutes to complete the task.

At some previous moment, you will have made the stuffing for the quenelles. (This is what makes the stuffing "double".) It consists of the milt of the fish and the sweetbreads of the lamb, both the neck and stomach varieties. (Don't forget to mention *them* to your butcher.) The milt is rapidly blanched. The sweetbreads are diced, salted, spiced with freshly ground hot pepper, and tossed for 6 minutes in clarified butter. Both are then chopped very fine (blender permitted) and kneaded into an unctuous mass with the help of 1 cup of lamb marrow and 3 tbsp of aged Madeira.

I said at the outset that I am in favour of appropriate substitutions in preparing *farce double*: but even though one eminent authority has suggested it, stuffing the quenelles with banana peanut butter is not appropriate.

The quenelles must now be shaped. Some writers who have discoursed at length on the traditional Auvergnat shape urge its adoption at all costs. I disagree. For the inhabitants of La Tour Lambert, who attach great significance to *farce double*, it may be right to feel strongly on this point. The same cannot be said for families in Maplewood or Orange County. You have enough to worry about as it is. If you are, however, an incurable stickler, you should know that in Auvergne moulds are used. They are called *beurdes* (they are, coincidentally, shaped like birds), and they are available here. You can find them in any of the better head shops.

But forget about bird moulds. Slap your fish paste on to a board and roll it flat. Spread on stuffing in parallel ½-inch bands 2 inches apart. Cut paste midway between bands, roll these strips into cylinders, and slice the cylinders into sections no larger than a small headache. Dip each piece in truffle crumbs. (See TRUFFLE.)

I refuse to become involved in the pros and cons of pre-steaming the quenelles. The only steam in La Tour Lambert is a rare fragrant wisp from the dampened fire of a roasting pit.

We now approach a crux in the preparation of *farce double*: enveloping the quenelles and binding them into the lamb. I must make a stern observation here; and you must listen to it. You must take it absolutely to heart.

If the traditional ways of enveloping the quenelles are arduous, they are in no way gratuitous. On them depends an essential component of *farce double*, namely the subtle interaction of lamb and fish. While the quenelles (and the poaching liquid that bathes them) must be largely insulated from the encompassing meat, they should not be wholly so. The quenelles must not be drenched in roasting juice or the lamb in fishy broth, but an exchange should occur, definite no matter how mild. Do not *under any circumstances* use a baggie or Saran Wrap to enfold the quenelles. Of course it's easier. So are TV dinners. For once, demand the utmost of yourself: the satisfaction will astound you, and *there is no other way.*

I mentioned this misuse of plastic to a native of La Tour Lambert. My interlocutor, as if appealing for divine aid, leaned back, lifted up his eyes, and stretched forth his arms. He was standing at the edge of a marinating trough; its edges were slick with marinade. One foot shot forward, he teetered for one moment on the brink, and then down he went. Dripping oil, encrusted with fragrant herbs, he emerged briskly and burst into tears.

There are two methods. I shall describe the first one briefly: it is the one used by official cooks for public banquets. Cawl (tripe skin) is scraped free of fat and rubbed with pumice-stone to a thinness approaching non-existence. This gossamer is sewn into an open pouch, which is filled with the quenelles and broth before being sewn shut. The sealing of the pouch is preposterously difficult. I have tried it six times; each time, ineluctable burstage has ensued. Even the nimble-fingered, thimble-thumbed seamstresses of La Tour Lambert find it hard. In their floodlit corner of the festal cave, they are surrounded by a sizeable choir of wailing boys whose task is to aggravate their intention to a pitch of absolute sustained concentration. If the miracle always occurs, it is never less than miraculous.

The second method is to seal the quenelles inside a clay shell. This demands no supernatural skills, merely attention.

Purveyors of reliable cooking clay now exist in all major cities. The best are Italian. In New York, the most dependable are to be found in east Queens. (For addresses, see APPENDIX.)

Stretch and tack down two 18-inch cheesecloth squares. Sprinkle until soaking (mop up puddles, however). Distribute clay in pats and roll flat until entire surface is evenly covered. The layer of clay should be no more than 1/16-inch thick. Scissor edges clean.

Drape each square on an overturned 2-qt bowl. Fold back flaps. Mould into hemispheres. Check fit, then dent edge of each hemisphere with forefinger so that when dents are facing each other, they form a ¾-inch hole.

Be sure to prepare the shell at least 48 hours in advance so that it hardens properly. (If you are a potter, you can bake it in the oven; if not, you risk cracking.) As the drying clay flattens against the cheesecloth, tiny holes will appear. Do *not* plug them. Little will pass through them: just enough to allow the necessary exchange of savours.

Make the poaching liquid — 3 qts of it — like ordinary fish stock (q.v.). The wine used for this in Auvergne is of a local sparkling variety not on the market; but any good champagne is an acceptable substitute.

By "acceptable substitute", I mean one acceptable to me. Purists have cited the fish stock as a reason for not making *farce double* at all. In La Tour Lambert, they rightly assert, the way the stock is kept allows it to evolve without spoiling: in the amphora-like jars that are stored in the coldest depths of the great cave, a faint, perpetual fermentation gives the perennial brew an exquisite, violet-flavoured sourness. This, they say, is inimitable. *I* say that 30 drops of decoction of elecampane blossoms will reproduce it so perfectly as to convince the most vigilant tongue.

Fifteen minutes before roasting time, put the quenelles in one of the clay hemispheres. Set the other against it, dent to dent. Seal the seam with clay, except for the hole, and thumb down well. Hold the sphere in one hand with the hole on top. With a funnel, pour in *hot* poaching liquid until it overflows, then empty I cup of liquid. This is to keep the shell from bursting from within when the broth reaches a boil.

Be sure to keep the shell in your hand: set in a bowl, one bash against its side will postpone your dinner for several days at least. In La Tour Lambert, where even more fragile gut is used, the risks are lessened by placing the diaphanous bags in woollen reticules. It is still incredible that no damage is ever done to them on the way to the stuffing tables. To avoid their cooling, they are carried at a run by teenage boys, for whom this is a signal honour: every Sunday throughout the following year, they will be allowed to wear their unmistakable lily-white smocks.

Earlier in the day, you will have anointed the lamb, inside and out: inside, with fresh basil, coriander leaves, garlic, and ginger thickly crushed into walnut oil (this is a *must*); outside, with mustard powder mixed with — ideally — wild-boar fat. I know that wild boars do not roam our woods (sometimes, on my walks through Central Park, I feel I may soon meet one): bacon fat will do — about a pint of it.

You will have left the lamb lying outside down. Now nestle the clay shell inside the boneless cavity. Work it patiently into the fleshy nooks, then urge the meat in little bulges around it, pressing the lamb next to the shell, not against it, with the gentlest possible nudges. When the shell is deeply ensconced, fold the outlying flaps over it, and shape the whole into a regular square cushion roast. Sew the edges of the meat together, making the seams hermetically tight.

If the original roasting conditions will surely exceed your grasp, a description of them may clarify your goals.

In Auvergne, the body of the lamb is lowered on wetted ropes into a roasting pit. It comes to rest on transverse bars set close to the floor of the pit. Hours before, ash boughs that have dried through three winters are heaped in the pit and set ablaze: by now they are embers. These are raked against the four sides and piled behind wrought-iron grids into glowing walls. The cast-iron floor stays hot from the fire. When the lamb is in place, a heated iron lid is set over the pit. The lid does more than refract the heat from below. Pierced with a multitude of small holes, it allows for aspersions of water on coals that need damping and the sprinkling of oil on the lamb, which is thus basted throughout its roasting in a continuous fine spray. Previously, I might add, the lamb has been rapidly seared over an open fire. Four senior cooks manage this by standing on high step-ladders and manipulating the poles and extensible thongs used to shift the animal, which they precisely revolve over the flames so that it receives an even grilling.

Thus the onslaught of heat to which the lamb is subjected is, while too restrained to burnt it, intense enough to raise the innermost broth to the simmering point.

Carefully lower the lamb into a 25-inch casserole. (If you have no such casserole, buy one. If it will not fit in your oven, consider this merely one more symptom of the shoddiness of our age, which the popularity of dishes like *farce double* may someday remedy.) Cover. You will have turned on the oven at maximum heat for 45 minutes at least. Close the oven door and lower the thermostat to 445°. For the next 5 hours, there is nothing to do except check the oven thermometer occasionally and baste the roast with juices from the casserole every 10 minutes. If you feel like catnapping, have no compunctions about it. Do *not* have anything to drink — considering what lies in store for you, it is a foolish risk. The genial cooks of La Tour Lambert may fall to drinking, dancing, and singing at this point, but remember that they have years of experience behind them; and you, unlike them, must act alone.

One song always sung during the roasting break provides valuable insight into the character of the Auvergnat community. It tells the story of a blacksmith's son who sets out to find his long-lost mother. She is dead, but he cannot remember her death, nor can he accept it. His widowed father has taken as second wife a pretty woman younger than himself. She is hardly motherly towards her stepson: one day, after he has grown to early manhood, she seduces him — in the words of the song, "she does for him what mother never did for her son". This line recurs throughout as a refrain.

It is after the shock of this event that the son leaves in quest of his mother. His father repeatedly tries to dissuade him, insisting that she is dead, or that, if she is alive, it is only in a place "as near as the valley beyond the hill and far away as the stars". In the end, however, he gives his son a sword and a purse full of money and lets him go. The stepmother, also hoping to keep the son from leaving, makes another but this time futile attempt to "do for him what mother never did for her son".

At the end of three days, the son comes to a city. At evening he meets a beautiful woman with long red hair. She offers him hospitality, which he accepts, and she attends lovingly to his every want. Pleasure and hope fill his breast. He begins wondering. He asks himself if this woman might not be his lost mother. But when night falls, the red-haired woman takes him into her bed and "does for him what mother never did for her son". The son knows she cannot be the one he seeks. Pretending to sleep, he waits for an opportunity to leave her; but, at midnight, he sees her draw a length of strong, sharp cord from beneath her pillow and stretch it towards him. The son leaps up, seizes his sword, and confronts the woman. Under its threat, she confesses that she was planning to murder him for the sake of his purse, as she has done with countless travellers: their corpses lie rotting in her cellar. The son slays the woman with his sword, wakes up a nearby priest to assure a Christian burial for her and her victims, and goes his way.

Three days later, he arrives at another city. As day wanes, a strange woman again offers him hospitality, and again he accepts. She is even more beautiful than the first; and her hair is also long, but golden. She lavishes her attentions on the young man, and in such profusion that hope once again spurs him to wonder whether she might not be his lost mother. But with the coming of darkness, the woman with the golden hair takes him into her bed and "does for him what mother never did for her son". His hopes have again been disappointed. Full of unease, he feigns sleep. Halfway through the night he hears footsteps mounting the stairs. He scarcely has time to leap out of bed and grasp his sword before two burly villains come rushing into the room. They attack him, and he cuts them down. Then, turning on the woman, he forces her at swordpoint to confess that she had hoped to make him her prisoner and sell him into slavery. Saracen pirates would have paid a high price for one of such strength and beauty. The son slays her, wakes up a priest to see that she and her henchmen receive Christian burial, and goes his way.

Another three days' journey brings him to a third city. There, at end of day, the son meets still another fair woman, the most beautiful of all, with flowing, raven-black hair. Alone of the three, she seems to recognise him; and when she takes him under her roof and bestows on him more comfort and affection than he had ever dreamed possible, he knows that this time his hope cannot be mistaken. But when night comes, she takes him into her bed, and she, like the others, "does for him what mother never did for her son". She has drugged his food. He cannot help falling asleep; only, at midnight, the touch of cold iron against his throat rouses him from his stupor. Taking up his sword, he points it in fury at the breast of the woman who has so beguiled him. She begs him to leave her in peace, but she finally acknowledges that she meant to cut his throat and suck his blood. She is an old, old witch who has lost all her powers but one, that of preserving her youth. This she does by drinking the blood of young men. The son runs her through with his sword. With a weak cry, she falls to the floor a wrinkled crone. The son knows that a witch cannot be buried in consecrated ground, and he goes his way.

But the young man travels no further. He is bitterly convinced of the folly of his quest; he has lost all hope of ever finding his mother; wearily he turns homeward.

On his way he passes through the cities where he had first faced danger. He is greeted as a hero. Thanks to the two priests, all know that it was he who destroyed the evil incarnate in their midst. But he takes no pride in having killed two women who "did for him what mother never did for her son".

On the ninth day of his return, he sees, from the mountain pass he has reached, the hill beyond which his native village lies. In the valley between, a shepherdess is watching her flock. At his approach she greets him tenderly, for she knows the blacksmith's son and has loved him for many years. He stops with her to rest. She has become, he notices, a beautiful young woman — not as beautiful, perhaps, as the evil three: but her eyes are wide and deep, and her long hair is brown.

The afternoon goes by. Still the son does not leave. At evening, he partakes of the shepherdess's frugal supper. At night-time, when she lies down, he lies down beside her; and she, her heart brimming with gladness, "does for him what mother never did for her son". The shepherdess falls asleep. The son cannot sleep; and he is appalled, in the middle of the night, to see the shepherdess suddenly rise up beside him. But she only touches his shoulder as if to waken him and points to the starry sky. She tells him to look up. There, she says, beyond the darkness, the souls of the dead have gathered into one blazing light. With a cry of pain, the son asks, "Then is my mother there?" The shepherdess answers that she is. His mother lives beyond the stars, and the stars themselves are chinks in the night through which the fateful light of the dead and the unborn is revealed to the world. "Oh, Mother, Mother", the young man weeps. The shepherdess then says to him, "Who is now mother to your sleep and waking? Who else can be the mother of your joy and pain? I shall henceforth be the mother of every memory; and from this night on, I alone am your mother — even if now, and tomorrow, and all the days of my life, I do for you what mother never did for her son." In his sudden ecstasy, the blacksmith's son understands. He has discovered his desire.

And so, next morning, he brings the shepherdess home. His father, when he sees them, weeps tears of relief and joy; and his stepmother, sick with remorse, welcomes them as saviours. Henceforth they all live in mutual contentment; and when, every evening, the approach of darkness kindles new yearning in the young man's heart and he turns to embrace his wife, she devotedly responds and never once fails, through the long passing years, to "do for him what mother never did for her son".

The connection of this song with *farce double* lies, I was told, in an analogy between the stars and the holes in the lid of the roasting pit.

When your timer sounds for the final round, you must be in fighting trim: not aggressive, but supremely alert. You now have to work at high speed and with utmost delicacy. The meat will have swelled in cooking: it is pressing against the clay shell harder than ever, and one jolt can spell disaster. Do not coddle yourself by thinking that this pressure is buttressing the shell. In La Tour Lambert, the handling of the cooked lamb is entrusted to squads of highly trained young men: they are solemn as pallbearers and dextrous as shortstops, and their virtuosity is eloquent proof that this is no time for optimism.

Slide the casserole slowly out of the oven and gently set it down on a table covered with a thrice-folded blanket. You will now need help. Summon anyone — a friend, a neighbour, a husband, a lover, a sibling, even a guest — so that the two of you can slip four broad wooden spatulas under the roast, one on each side, and ease it on to a platter. The platter should be resting on a soft surface such as a cushion or a mattress (a small hammock would be perfect). Wait for the meat to cool before moving it on to anything harder. Your assistant may withdraw.

Meanwhile attend to the gravy. No later than the previous evening, you will have made 1½ qts of stock with the bones from the lamb shoulder, together with the customary onions, carrots, celery, herb bouquet, cloves, scallions, parsnips, and garlic (see STOCK), to which you must not hesitate to add any old fowl, capon, partridge, or squab carcasses that are gathering rime in your deep freeze, or a young rabbit or two. Pour out the fat in the casserole and set it on the stove over high heat. Splash in enough of the same good champagne to scrape the casserole clean, and boil. When the wine has largely evaporated, take off heat, and add 2 cups of rendered pork fat. Set the casserole over very low heat and make a quick *roux* or brown sauce with 3 cups of flour. Then slowly pour in 2 cups of the blood of the lamb, stirring it in a spoonful at a time. Finally, add the stock. Raise the heat to medium high and let the liquid simmer down to the equivalent of 13 cupfuls.

While the gravy reduces, carefully set the platter with the roast on a table, resting one side on an object the size of this cookbook, so that it sits at a tilt. Place a broad shallow bowl against the lower side. If the clay shell now breaks, the poaching broth will flow rapidly into the bowl. Prop the lamb with a wooden spoon or two to keep it from sliding off the platter.

Slit the seams in the meat, spread its folds, and expose the clay shell. Put on kitchen gloves — the clay will be scalding — and coax the shell from its depths. Set it in a saucepan, give it a smart crack with a mallet, and remove the grosser shards. Ladle out the quenelles and keep them warm in the oven in a covered, buttered dish with a few spoonfuls of broth. Strain the rest of the liquid, reduce it quickly to a quarter of its volume, and then use what is left of the champagne to make a white sauce as explained on p. 888. Nap the quenelles with sauce and serve.

If you have worked fast and well, by the time your guests finish the quenelles, the lamb will have set long enough for its juices to have withdrawn into the tissues without its getting cold. Pour the gravy into individual heated bowls. Place a bowl in front of each guest, and set the platter with the lamb, which you will have turned outside up, at the centre of the table. The meat is eaten without knives and forks. Break off a morsel with the fingers of the right hand, dip it in gravy, and pop it into your mouth. In Auvergne, this is managed with nary a dribble; but lobster bibs are a comfort.

(Do not be upset if you yourself have lost all desire to eat. This is a normal, salutary condition. Your satisfaction will have been in the doing, not in the thing done. But observe the reaction of your guests, have a glass of wine [see below], and you may feel the urge to try one bite, and perhaps a second . . .)

It is a solemn moment when, at the great communal spring banquet, the mayor of La Tour Lambert goes from table to table and with shining fingers gravely breaks the skin of each lamb, After this ceremony, however, the prevailing gaiety reasserts itself. After all, the feast of *farce double* is not only a time-hallowed occasion but a very pleasant one. It is a moment for friendships to be renewed, for enemies to forgive one another, for lovers to embrace. At its origin, curiously enough, the feast was associated with second marriages (some writers think this gave the dish its name). Such marriages have never been historically explained; possibly they never took place. What is certain is that the feast has always coincided with the arrival, from the lowlands, of shepherds driving their flocks to the high pastures where they will summer. Their coming heralds true spring and its first warmth; and it restores warmth, too, between the settled mountain crafts-men of La Tour Lambert and the semi-nomadic shepherds from the south. The two communities are separate only in their ways of life. They have long been allied by esteem, common interest, and, most important, by blood. Marriages between them have been recorded since the founding of the village in the year one thousand; and if many a shepherd's daughter has settled in La Tour Lambert as the wife of a wheelwright or turner, many an Auvergnat son, come autumn, has left his father's mill or forge to follow the migrant flocks towards Les Saintes-Maries-de-la-Mer. Perhaps the legend of second marriages reflects a practice whereby a widow or a widower took a spouse among the folk of which he was not a member. The eating of *farce double* would then be exquisitely appropriate; for there is no doubt at all that the composition of the dish — lamb from the plains by the sea, fish from lakes among the grazing lands — deliberately embodies the merging of these distinct peoples in one community. I should add that at the time the feast originated, still another group participated harmoniously in its celebration: pilgrims from Burgundy on their way to Santiago de Compostela. Just as the people of La Tour Lambert provided fish for the great banquet and the shepherds contributed their lambs, the pilgrims supplied kegs of new white wine that they brought with them from Chassagne, the Burgundian village now called Chassagne-Montrachet. Their wine became the invariable accompaniment for both parts of *farce double*; and you could hardly do better than to adopt the custom. Here, at least, tradition can be observed with perfect fidelity.

It is saddening to report that, like the rest of the world, La Tour Lambert has undergone considerable change. Shepherds no longer walk their flocks from the south but ship them by truck. The lakes have been fished out, and a substitute for *chaste* is imported frozen from Yugoslavia. The grandson of the last wheelwright works in the tourist bureau, greeting latter-day pilgrims who bring no wine. He is one of the very few of his generation to have remained in the village. (The cement quarry, which was opened with great fanfare ten years ago as a way of providing jobs, employs mainly foreign labour. Its most visible effect has been to shroud the landscape in white dust.) I have heard, however, that the blacksmith still earns a good living making wrought-iron lamps. Fortunately, the future of *farce double* is assured, at least for the time being. The festal cave has been put on a commercial footing, and it now produces the dish for restaurants in the area all year round (in the off season, on weekends only). It is open to the public. I recommend a visit if you pass nearby.

Eat the quenelles ungarnished. Mashed sorrel goes nicely with the lamb.

Serves thirteen.

1977

25

THE WAY HOME

Drawings by Trevor Winkfield

Imagination moves by angles, along a black line inscribed on a white ground that is itself bordered by blackness. The mind rests when it comes to identifiable objects athwart or alongside this line: chewable wood pellets, for instance, or a woman catching minnows. The imagination then faces, after many other obstacles, a choice it cannot avoid: whether to engage the identifiable object — that is, face its identity as a clear or coded sign that will help the imagination round the next angle — or to accept it as no more than an occasion for rest, something to lean an elbow on while drawing fresh and not necessarily metaphorical breath. For instance, the woman catching minnows may be simply an image of pleasantly inconsequential country work, hardly significant to the passer-by except as a pretext for pastoral-minded relaxation (an effect heightened by the skirts drawn up in her right hand above her bright, reflected knees); or she may turn to him and speak.

One class of objects provides the imagination with peculiar confusion and, perhaps, opportunity: the class of objects that can be recognised but not named, that strike the voyager as having every right to claim a place in the real world (the real world of the imagination) but whose context he cannot remember or conceive of. Think of a rectangular box whose six sides, made of composition board, are separated from each other by spaces five-eighths of an inch across. No magnet, twine, or loosened screw connects them, and yet the box keeps its shape in front of our eyes without straining our reason or our belief.

Can we associate objects such as this with the moment in which desire is conceived? Are they desire's catalysts or its companions?

In the real world, the real world of the imagination, the appearance of such objects operates, or allows the voyager to operate, a reversal of elements: for example, day will turn to night, and not necessarily the night of dreams. More simply, darkness will replace light, as though the white ground, out of some sublimely appropriate courtesy, had surrendered to the blackness bordering it. No loss is felt at this moment, and no confusion. The reversal and the surrender produce, it is true, a surprisingly new context, but clearly this context has been created in response to an imperious need. The voyager knows that in the reality of his imagination he cannot hope to understand his need except through an exploration of the context that has been created for this very purpose. So he has no sense of confusion. He may have a sense of desire, and of the fear that goes with desire (that school of flitting minnows). More probably, he has little sense of anything except the darkness that gives the new object such frosty brightness.

At times objects will distract and finally disappoint him. They will give rise to graceful or interesting explanations. Thus a group of inanimate, irregular solids will be seen through a screen of swaying vines, and the traveller, who has after all not slept for days or years or even since the time of his birth, will rest his eyes (and his nose, his tongue) on these vines, becoming ridiculously pleased with himself when he discovers they are not vines at all but the little green clusters of bastard toadflax or the slender blackish stalks of some fern he remembers from moister, warmer climes. He forgets the chewable wood pellets.

Mr. Maltmall had spent the greater part of his life, perhaps every moment since his birth, in shadowy, imaginary voyage. He flitted precariously at the hub of time's wheel like a hummingbird motionlessly voyaging at the centre of a spoked, nameless flower. The spokes of the flower sharpened his engagement with life, hovering pointedly on the periphery of his vision like the figures on a clock face or the circle of constellations on an astrological calendar. They reminded him that he had committed himself to a ceremonial of limited duration, so that while they did not confine him, out of the knowledge of his finiteness he kept his enthusiasm at a whirring pitch, like a partisan mounting guard on a quiet night in territory occupied by the oppressor, like a mandarin rewriting salutary laws that neglect and misrule have left a shambles.

He held himself straight, with a slight bend of alertness in his knees. Not lean or fat, he gave an impression of despondent strength, with his wide, bent shoulders. His beard, once thoroughly black, had turned brownish and was mixed with sparse white hairs. When he was offended, his lips and the tip of his nose looked blue against his florid face. He gestured and walked with considerable slowness, as if not to offend in turn. He spoke in a harsh, broad voice pitched agreeably low.

Sometimes, as he considered deeds, prospectuses, contracts, an apparition would form in the chinks of the print, delineated by the cascade of spaces flowing through terms of payment and mortgage allowances. (The words by no means bored him, lively as they were with promises of building, exchange, and newly roofed lives.) Amidst these technicalities first a white haze, then a white possibility emerged in the background of the page: a waterside of reeds and redwing blackbirds, sun-warmed shallows glittering beyond, apparently roiled by the swoop of an oar — but it was too shallow there for an oar, something else was being dragged through the fertile water, a pole, or the bared foot of a wader. Beyond the reeds, beyond the fine bunched type, Mr. Maltmall assembled an event out of whiteness and light, the way a starwatcher connects a constellation from dispersed bunches of stars.

The scene he had thus encountered or constructed in his attentive, imaginary travels provoked a sense in him less of desire than of hopeful curiosity. He felt that something new had been promised him, new, agreeable, and perhaps illuminating. The promise immediately restored his gift for noticing small, attractive anomalies in the course of his ordinary life. At lunch his place was set with a fork to the left of his plate, another fork to the right of his plate. On his way to the beach, a short clothes-line sagged inexplicably with the weight of a single stiff, fluffy diaper.

Some of his friends were already smacking a ball over the volleyball net set up on a level area of off-white sand. "Walt the Malt!" they cried when they saw him. He took his place among them. His team-mates appreciated the sharp, accurate smashes that he made using the side of his fist. He played willingly enough, although he was never completely absorbed by the game. He liked best the moments when he tossed the ball high in the air to serve and looked up into the hazy summer sky. That afternoon, turning away from the net after a point-winning smash, he saw a boy and a girl down the beach hitting a shuttlecock back and forth in high, slow parabolas and wished that he could join them.

The whipped paddle, the shuttlecock's lazy flight: real play. After the team changed sides, the children were constantly in view. The sun drooped behind dunes; one swipe sailed the white-plastic feathers into its tilted rays, which seemed to catch and hold them at the apogee of their flight. Walt was reminded of a high note near the end of a solo by John Coltrane, sustained with sweetly inhuman intensity. The volleyball hit Walt on the nose. He clenched his eyes. In blackness, lines of brilliant light streamed outwards from a twirling, shadowy centre that he longed to cling to, at least until his nose forgave him. He wiped his eyes. Bouncing from his face, the ball had been retrieved by an alert team-mate. He had not lost the point. It was his turn to serve.

Subsiding twinges in his buffeted eyes looped red, readable strands against the gold-showered sky: an old woman with a staff was prodding three sheep towards

a marketplace. He blinked and tapped the ball far into the opposite court. The red scene, quickly gone, recalled to him the morning's waterside apparition. It had been very different. The red scene held no promise, he knew it at once to be only a relic of some childhood story, of no use to him now even as a place to rest and breathe. The battledore partners were calling it a day.

The air cooled, and evening cooled the tones around him — pale grey sand, blue-grey ocean, black-and-whitening grass, the volleyball black when tossed against the sky. Walt Maltmall: he silently pronounced his name with bitterness and contempt. Playing ball looked to him like playing at still-growing childhood; he resembled rather the aged, dishevelled, waddling gull that was methodically exploring litter on the empty beach. After his friends said goodbye, he shut his eyes, making literal his feeling that he was losing his sight, his feeling that the only living sensation in him was a thoroughly blind urge to follow something — something that was running away from him, something tender that might be caught, torn to pieces, eaten, held against his tearless cheeks. He hated this urge, which had the reddish blackness of rage, and hated his self-hatred. Stars faded against the maroon depths of his eyelids.

Fading or not, the stars restored a sense of space outside the restricted corridor of his imagined pursuit. He considered the new space opening around him, soon huge enough, and the objects it presented as they slid past him. He saw a baby fastened to the nipple of an adolescent girl's breast, poking it compulsively and regularly with tiny fists. The capital letter S stood alone and high against a landscape of pale orchards and vine-covered hillslopes. A solitary joker in cap and bells lay on a wooden table painted a brownish shade of maroon. His father was showing him how to thread a rod used for fly fishing. An ad he had once placed in the Sunday *Times* displayed a photograph of a thirty-room shingle house with broad lawns surrounding it. Seen from behind, a young woman dextrously plugged and unplugged the connections of a hotel switchboard. A cake encrusted with green rock candy proposed a bright red plum at its centre.

There is no object so soft but that it makes a hub of the wheeled universe. There is no shadow so slow but that it makes a wing of the wheeling soul. There is no thought so precarious but that it makes a word of the drenched shadow. There is no pit so shallow but that it makes a chasm of the sensible intelligence. There is no drink so wet but that it makes a desert of the dying voice. There is no sonatina so short but that it makes a fluency of the chartered streets. There is no brood so scattered but that it makes a hearth of the dying miser. There is no man, no woman so lost but that she makes a goal of the attentive will. No book so sold but that it makes an expectation of an obsolescent barman. No dish so bland but that it makes a lesson of the deserving dog. No Walt so Malt but that he makes a shadow of the universal wheel.

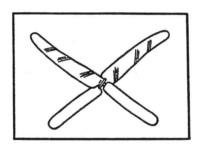

And that woman, that young woman picking mallows, if that is what she's doing — in a vague way, he dreaded banishing her to the hillsides, where he would no longer hear the fretting of her corduroyed inner thighs. He had reached an angle of his black line and was afraid of becoming stuck there. He did not want to rely on her to help him around the angle, to turn his journeying gaze down the next stretch of black band. What he somewhat less vaguely imagined he had to do to negotiate the turn was to step away from what lay in front of him, to turn his back on it and then keep turning until he had swung around into the direction of the next straight passage. He imagined her helping him if he chose this more extensive but more yielding shift on to his new course. She would broaden or even complete his intended revolution by providing an angle of darkness equal to his own darkness. Addressing it, he might have to relinquish breathing completely, his mouth buried in blackish fern, his nose pinched in her pleasurable native grasp. Such symmetry made no sense, it meant not vaguely but precisely dark to dark, his eyes (whether open or shut) also stifled by beach balls — hers. He followed her into the hills.

Deep into the night, he told himself that he had no excuse not to be at work on time. His imaginary journeying demanded actual common-or-garden movement, not sitting around contemplating the situation. Perceptions came as accessories to keeping appointments, to reading the fine print. Movement meant shuttling day after day between familiar places, which all the same were tinged with a kind of mental dye if they promised to coincide with his secret itinerary of desire. It had been the same during his childhood when places to go meant the rooms of his parents' apartment or at most the buildings on his grandmother's farm. His grandmother had built a sheepfold with a protective cupola over it and had painted the cupola with green polka dots scattered across a coal-black field. Walt as a boy knew the minute he saw it that the covered fold would be a refuge; and he soon settled himself inside it in moments of neglect, crouching and daydreaming among stuffy ewes and lambs, many of them shorn and ticketed for sale and slaughter.

Was there truly a black angled line, inscribed on a white background, along which he perceptibly moved? Or was he still at his point of departure, the readiness for departure forming the substance of his life rather than any calculably real advance? He pictured himself as a runner in an everlasting crouch, one foot on the starting-block; or launched into a first stride, neither foot touching the ground and destined never to touch the ground. Whom was he racing against? All those he knew stood behind him or along the nearby sidelines, while those he imagined knowing were waiting on the far side of the finish line.

A foot straining with the promise of motion: can that ever be called motion? Shouldn't the foot disappear entirely in the swift blurred revolution of the runners stride (and there was no stride either, only the race)? Walt said to himself, and to some others, "I say that's what it's all about." Then why did he insist on feeling like a mere foot, and sometimes like a shoe, full of the best and most useful intentions?

He lay down in the moist, black ferns. He had hoped to reach a lake, but he'd stumbled into this marsh in the darkness, which fell so quickly these mid-September days. He didn't really mind. The marsh mud was lake-bottom mud in its warm clayiness and its sweet, mulchy smell. He wiggled his fingers and toes into it, his nose, his pelvis, and at last his tongue. (He expected the mud to taste shittily bitter; it proved almost bland.) He bit down into the clay. He thought: now stop breathing, keep burrowing your face into this muck, let yourself go, let it all go. Would that be so bad? The mud still kept some of the sun's warmth, its squelchiness was consolation made matter. Where else is there to go? And if I go there, how will I explain the way I look?

He nestled in the mud bed like a shoetree inside a closeted black shoe. He knew he could not stay there. He had lost the least intention of motion, of travel, he had forgotten the daylight and the succession of amusing days. He became aware of this himself because against the dark lining of his eyelids he saw nothing but mudlike darkness. He was enjoying himself. He found it ecstatically soothing to be able to look at what could not be called nothing, since there was a blankly black something there, but a something shorn of every physical and metaphysical detail, a mass of empty soft flat indifferent darkness. When he was through enjoying himself (a moment he had to pick wilfully), he stood up out of the mud and returned to the living world of his imagination.

So much remains to be told, so much remains to be disguised in order to be told. The image of the black shoe cannot be right, even to describe a condition of solitude. There is never a condition of solitude. It is as if a cat arrived in a town and

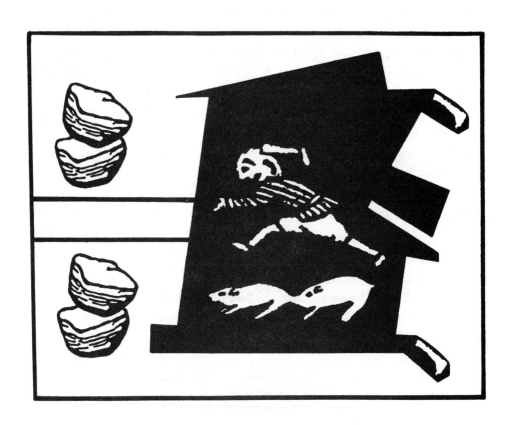

discovers that it has become a ghost town. Signs along the main street indicate that the town is now in the power of mouse ghosts, who threaten all cats with suffering and death. And the newcomer cat is duly made to suffer and die. He becomes a ghost in turn; he is thus able to reassert his predominance over the mice who had so gleefully persecuted him. So Walt Maltmall, glittering blackly with the muck of oblivion, returned with no apparent stealth to his bungalow and breakfast.

A moment occurs in the dawn twilight when the oppression of darkness and the oppression of light are symmetrical, although our dread of light is greater because we know it now threatens us. At that moment Walt diverted himself with abstract concepts, like dialectic, process, or signification. These concepts became or replaced the familiar wayside objects of the category "things to lean against". To emerge from this state of abstraction, Walt needed certain omens: a red knot, a patch of windlessness, an agreeable stench, something conspicuously if loosely recurrent, like the repositionings of a lawnmower outside the deli he was now passing. He could conveniently adapt what he came across (the knot could be one in a painted board) but he needed to focus on these reassuringly tangible things in order to realign the disordered self he had knowingly left to one side when he resorted to generalities.

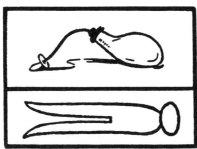

Walt was modern enough in his way. He knew that the money he made was no more than worldly acknowledgement of his commitment to playing the work game. He disliked poker because, when he played the game, he resented having his decisions judged according to the same principle. (He also hated losing.) He knew perfectly well that work and play were fictions, mirror-faceted shoes on the runner's feet; whereas knees, nude and evasive, promised more genuine significances.

But when Walt began looking for omens, he found his awareness obfuscated by anticipations of matters and people to be dealt with during his forthcoming day — matters of money and pride. The anticipations then revived memories: memories not of material events but of old fantasies, which replayed themselves as black-and-white movies in an utterly dark, undefined space. Once, taking the form of an adolescent girl, he opens the door of the guest room and finds his grandparents in gravely ecstatic copulation. The young girl does not know whether to shut the door as softly as she opened it or to drape herself like a film of cream across their grizzled bodies. Their grizzled hair and skin have stirred her by reminding her of the skin on the faces of ewes as they entered a domed fold at twilight. In another movie he finds himself in a junkyard littered with battered although almost new pie tins and old knives of widely differing sizes but identical design. This movie has an obsessive voice-over: "The very word is like a knell, the very word is like a knell . . ."

As he approached home the needed omens manifested themselves. When he reached his front door he spent a moment looking through the peep-hole, which offered him a slightly blurred but undistorted view of the interior, with at its centre the ball on the newel post, reflective as a mirror, shadowy as a closed eye. He was looking forward to his breakfast, after possibly a quick wash-up: frozen tangerine juice, Del Monte peaches, instant coffee with a drop of Carnation milk in it (remember not to cheat and suck a delectable jet out of the punctured can), a cigarette between coffees, the smoke at his elbow rising tenuous and straight towards the ceiling. He longed to have a mutt that would sidle up to him at such moments and lie across his feet. He was aware at the same time of bristling with aversions to all the pure and impure dog breeds of the world. He opened the front door and entered his home contentedly. He stopped to consider his barely distinguishable reflection in the varnished globe on the newel post: it looked like his memory movies before they coalesced into objects limp or stiff.

He took off his mudcaked shoes, washed off the mud, filled their insteps with crumpled newspaper, and set them out on the west deck to dry. He straightened up too quickly after putting them down, so that the blood drained out of his head and he had to lean on the railing of the deck. Shutting his eyes, he had a glimpse in the maroon darkness of the woman at the waterside, the minnow fisher, standing up to her ankles in the glittering pond. She raised her skirt to her hips, pointed her right leg a little to the side, and loosed a sun-spangled quivering shaft into the roiled water at her feet. And ever shalt thou yearn. At least he hoped to. Or rather he expected to look forward to — he mentally and quickly made the correction since he knew hope to be no more than a barb on the hook of desire; he had no intention of ending up like a trout on his father's line, even if he knew that soon he would be considerately released.

Miss Minnower! She probably got along with all kinds of dogs, knowing when to leash and unleash them, when to let them chase cats and when to let the cats chase them. If only she would look back, cast wide her arms, let her frizzled hair fall behind her ears and show her face to him and the generous sun! Teeth and all.

He knew that he must move on from this scene. It too now belonged to the past, the past of expectations. Nothing wrong with that. Halfway through his

peaches he sensed that light had begun shining on the path in front of him. The view remained one of gloom and murk, but he was fairly sure of a division of the dark greyness into lighter elements withdrawing right and left and blacker elements starting to concentrate in the centre of the picture, soon to become a way, his way. He sat and waited for more light, or more clarity, as though waiting for a roll of the dice in Monopoly, which as a boy he had played addictively if never with much intelligence.

He did not have to wait long. In the dissolving greyness a black band led straight ahead of him towards the next angle. He could even see what awaited him there: a familiar scene, a country fair, in the midst of which he noticed a broad, slowly turning wheel connected with some game of chance, a wheel segmented according to the succession of the constellations, with what seemed to be a captive plastic hummingbird fluttering in a shaft of air expelled from the centre of the wheel. He had barely started down the path when he felt a light tap on the side of his head. Looking round, he discovered his beloved grandmother in her red cloak and pointed red hat. She was leading him and his fellows to the fair, prodding him considerately behind his ticketed ear, leading them to the country fair past freshly winnowed fields.

1987

SINGULAR PLEASURES

Dressed in a cotton playsuit, an eleven-year-old girl is masturbating in an empty sitting-room in Glasgow. She is squatting astride a rugby ball, rocking back and forth at moderate speed. On the television set in front of her, running, barelegged rugby players keep smashing into one another. As she reaches a climax, she tilts the blunt tip of the ball hard against her pubis.

A man of sixty-eight years is lying on an unmade bed masturbating. The room, filled with packing cases and furniture in disorder, is in a beautiful house overlooking Cape Town; the man has just taken possession of it. Throughout his life, whenever he has moved, he has found that until he masturbated in a new dwelling he cannot think of it as home. His wife urges him to get on with it.

In Naha, Okinawa, a woman sixty years old is masturbating in front of her favourite cat, a female Siamese. The look of the cat as it watches her, curled at the foot of the mat on which she lies, suggests faintly baleful indifference. It is this look which excites the woman and is responsible for the cat's presence. It suddenly yawns — she dips into orgasm like a battered shrimp into sizzling oil.

A man of thirty-five is about to experience orgasm in one of the better condominiums in Gaza. He is masturbating, but neither hand nor object touches his taut penis: arranged in a circle, five hairblowers direct their streams of warm air towards that focal point. He has plugged his ears with wax balls.

Entering her Spokane kitchen in a state of sexual frenzy, a woman approaching thirty-three starts masturbating with every implement that comes to hand — bulb of turkey baster, tip of rolling-pin, kettle handle, salt shaker, rubber spatula, attachment of electric beater, lemon cone of rotary juicer — finding satisfaction at last with the turkey baster proper, filled with hot whipping cream.

The highland town of Kandy is one of the religious centres of Sri Lanka. There, on the veranda of an elegant bungalow, a woman in her thirties (her purplish ankle-length robe parted to reveal her swarthy, anointed body) stands looking down at a twenty-two-year-old Westerner masturbating on the floor in front of her. He lies smirched with the dust in which he writhes. He gazes up imploringly at the woman; whenever he moves towards her, she pushes him away with a long ceremonial staff. As his excitement comes to a head, she slides the point of the staff inside his thigh, under his testicles, prodding hard: semen rises towards her in an arc that is the inverse of her acute, ambiguous smile.

A native woman has disappeared into the jungle upstream from Manaus. She is alone. She wants to do what she had so often done until her fifteenth birthday, ten years before, when she became a woman: straddle once again the resilient trunk of a young rubber-band tree.

At the age of sixty-nine riding in a motor-boat for the first time, a citizen of Shanghai sneaks to the stern of the new municipal transit launch and quickly and compulsively masturbates into its muddy wake. He realises that he is subject to "bus fever": any conveyance that throbs with the vibrations of an internal-combustion engine will bring on in him an over-powering need for orgasm. He starts thinking with nostalgia of the Cultural Revolution and its Spartan ways.

A lady fifty-two years old who lives in the El-Guezireh section of Cairo calls — as she always does when she feels like masturbating — for her young Nubian maid. During the better part of her mistress's satin-sheeted wrigglings, the girl does no more than provide a kind of friendly witness. Towards the end, the lady requests that she rub her feet: "Smear them with nard", she cries, "think of each one as your lover's lazy penis!" The maid squeezes one foot, then the other. The two women soon start giggling — the lady comes to a climax in a duet of arpeggios and trills.

While staying with friends in Geneva, a man of thirty goes into the bathroom to shave: on the washbasin he discovers his first vibrator. The instrument has various attachments for massaging various parts of the body — the scalp, for instance. More out of curiosity than desire, he tests one of the attachments (designed for the female breast), a shallow rubber cone that he sets on the end of his penis. Turning on the machine he groans as the sperm is sucked out of him.

A woman in Hyderabad, because it is her birthday (her fifty-fifth), is masturbating for the very first time. It reminds her of breakfasts during the war with China, when her husband was away at the front.

While the Aeolian String Quartet performs the final variation of Haydn's "Emperor" Quartet in the smaller of Managua's two concert halls, a man of three score and four summers sits masturbating in the last row of the orchestra, a coat on his lap. Thirty-three years before, after relieving himself during the intermission of another concert, he had returned to his seat with his fly unbuttoned. Unconscious of his appearance, he had become erect during a scintillating performance of the Schubert Octet and actually ejaculated during the final chords. The house lights had come up to reveal his disarray; he had fled; ever since, he has been labouring steadfastly to recreate that momentary bliss.

In Leningrad, a fifty-eight-year-old woman, wearing only a night-gown that she has drawn up around her waist, is lying on a carpet next to her bed. In one hand she holds an electric toothbrush (with a tourist she has recently bartered half a pound of caviar for it); the fingers of her other hand fold the outer skin of her vulva over the vibrating tip of the brush. She turns the bristles inward against her clitoris: her features become twisted with feeling. She pisses a little at the point of orgasm. Turning off the appliance, she pulls down her night-gown and goes to bed.

Flat on his back, his wrists and ankles immobilised by cords, a young man watches his companion masturbating. The latter is a grey-haired man of fifty-four, who looks at the young man only once, when he turns to ejaculate across his thighs. He then dresses and goes out. Before leaving the hotel, he informs the chambermaid that she can make up his room whenever she likes. The streets of Tangiers are bright with early morning.

A young woman senses that her lover wants to ask her a favour. "Speak your desire!" she says. "To see you . . ." He hesitates, touches her hand. "Masturbate?" she says, then laughs and happily complies: "At your service!" But when she says, "Your turn!" he is paralysed with embarrassment. This ruins the pleasure he has felt watching her. An inhabitant of Gustavia (St. Bart's), he, like his companion, is only sixteen.

As he masturbates, a forty-five-year-old man in Pretoria is standing in front of a full-length mirror watching himself. On the far side of the two-way mirror, a woman of eighty-one sits looking at him, one hand busy beneath her skirts. The man ejaculates on to the mirror: she mutters, "Too soon!"

Lying on his bed, a man in Bahia has just finished masturbating for the first time in his eighteen years. He did not enjoy it.

Thirty-eight, divorced, mother of two sons, a woman is masturbating in her bedroom in Adelaide with a thick, supple dildo. She has resorted to the instrument after weeks of general chastity and is now using it to achieve her sixth consecutive orgasm. First she had simply rubbed its tip back and forth over her clitoris; then she had begun working the tip between the lips of her vagina while continuing to stroke her clitoris with its shaft; next, she had gone deeper, only touching her clitoris occasionally; after that, lying on her back with knees raised, she had thrust the instrument even farther inside her; she has just finished penetrating her vagina from behind, resting on her knees and one hand, with her free hand passed back between her legs; and she is now, finally — kneeling, her buttocks on her heels, her hands holding the massive body securely inside her — snapping her pelvis against it with a dancer's precision and strength. Soon she will put the dildo away in a shoebox on the top shelf of her closet and go back to correcting term papers.

When he masturbates, old Zakku — in fact he is only forty-seven — never bothers to hide anymore. To fellow tribesmen in this village south of Zizanga, he is known as "the White man".

A woman of thirty-nine, in an uncurtained bedroom in Calcutta, is being passionately caressed by another woman less than half her age. Eventually the older woman pushes her partner away and uses her own hand to satisfy herself. This is a pattern their lovemaking always follows; once again the young woman is left feeling frustrated and angry. She does not see that in this way the other holds her fast.

Somewhere north of the Bering Straits, sitting on the edge of an ice floe, his face impassive, all movement concealed beneath thicknesses of pelt and fur, an Eskimo male of thirty-one is bringing himself to an orgasm of devastating intensity in a slickness of dissolving blubber.

On her knees inside a confessional booth in the Seville cathedral, a twenty-one-year-old woman is describing her compulsive habit of masturbation. As the priest absolves her, she stands up, raises her skirt, and reveals that at this very moment she is committing the sin she has confessed.

A man is masturbating as he contemplates a finely brushed poem by Wang Wei, seated on a straw mat in his garret in Mukden. An "ascetic sensualist", he has striven all his life to unite in one moment of revelation the pleasures of poetry and masturbation. On this warm spring morning of his sixtieth year, he senses that the sublime fusion may finally be at hand.

The setting is a large hut in Luluabourg, a town of southern Zaire. A delegate from a woman's liberation organisation — a comely European of forty-eight — is demonstrating techniques of clitoral masturbation to a select representation of local tribeswomen. Her commentary is engulfed in squeals of hilarity and a clattering of prophylactic bones.

While waiting for help to arrive, a man is masturbating inside his car, which lies overturned in a ravine outside Erzurum, in eastern Turkey. At fifty no less than at twelve, he turns to masturbation whenever some unusual event — a subway train stopping between stations, theatre lights left dark while scenery is being changed — breaks the normal patterns of his life.

The near-freezing temperature delights the guard — a woman of sixty-one in charge of the top floor of the Catanzaro Museum of Fine Arts. Almost no one visits the museum, no one at all comes to her floor; and the cold will now justify wearing her heavy woollen coat, under whose cover she likes to sit and masturbate intermittently through winter days, gazing across the unheated gallery at a fervent and muscular Saint John the Baptist, the work of some nameless follower of Caravaggio.

Masturbating in the bedroom of his apartment, located in one of Seoul's nicer neighbourhoods, a man thirty-seven years old has surrounded himself with sumptuous appurtenances: blue lights of Venetian glass, incense from Saigon, the Flagstad *Liebestod* on Dolby, a baby-seal coverlet that is spread underneath him, clarified French butter lubricating his genitals and loins and easing the passage beneath his suspended knees of the ivory handle from a safari parasol that he is sliding between his buttocks, while his other hand teasingly strokes his glistening erection towards climax. . . He is watching himself in a mirror at the foot of his bed, he has sworn to keep watching to the bitter end, but as spasm overwhelms him his eyes snap helplessly shut, and the elaborate *mise en scène* vanishes at the very moment it has been designed to exalt.

A girl in Vancouver, aged twelve, is lying in a drained bath-tub directing the spurts of a Water Pik against her bared clitoris. The pulsing water keeps her deliciously short of orgasm. She many times refills the recipient from the faucets at the foot of the tub.

Aged seventy-eight and eighty, two brothers who are chartered members of a kibbutz near Rosh Pinna are arguing violently about each other's potency. When the younger accuses the elder of total impotence, the latter challenges him to a masturbation contest, which he wins handily, reaching orgasm in one minute forty-five seconds, scattering his seed to a distance of sixty-two centimetres.

In an elegant "privileged" apartment in the centre of Beijing, a nineteen-year-old woman is masturbating herself for the benefit of an elderly man, in turn standing, sitting, crouching, at all times turning towards him her vulva and anus, into which she slips tapering green lacquered fingers. After watching her for several minutes, the man tells her, "Enough play acting!" She lies down on the floor face up, locks her legs tight, and begins rubbing her slightly raised pubis fast and furiously with her downturned right thumb.

In a kitchen in Christchurch, New Zealand, a man on the threshold of thirty is pumping his bone-hard penis into a pack of raw sheep's liver that he clutches bloodily between his hands.

A man huge in girth and height has been heaving himself into the tiny body of a woman lying face down beneath him. With one hand between her legs she has vainly tried to bring herself to a climax that will coincide with his. He has ejaculated; he withdraws; soon, still sprawled on her, he falls asleep. The woman with prudent mildness begins masturbating herself again and in a while satisfies herself without waking her snoring man. Thus she begins her twenty-fourth year, in the dark of a night in Alma Ata.

A boy of thirteen sits masturbating on a toilet, in the vast empty lavatory of a boarding school near Valparaiso. He curses his addiction to this melancholy habit, wondering how it will affect his pimples.

Trying to photograph herself as she masturbates with a shocking-pink dildo on the living-room floor of a luxurious town house in Neuilly-sur-Seine, a beautiful woman of thirty-four is muttering to herself querulously. Doing two things at once is clearly too much for her — but which one should she choose?

Masturbating as he lies on a floor mat, his head propped on one hand, his eyes on a lighted television set, somewhere in Kyoto, there is a young man of twenty. The screen in front of him shows a young man lying on his side and masturbating while watching a television set on which a young man is lying on his side and masturbating while watching a television set on which a young man is lying on his side and masturbating while watching a television set whose image is too small to decipher.

". . . In France we used a glove from Grenoble, left empty for him, glove tongs inside it for me. In Russia, on the southern banks of the Volga, a sturgeon bereft of its roe for him, and for me the snout of the sturgeon. In Norway, the ski pole, and the hole in the snow (the latter requiring *layers* of preservatives) . . ." So reads a letter from this wife of fifty-three who, with her husband, three years her senior, decided one day to give up perfunctory lovemaking for the delights of parallel masturbation. Their idea was to use one object, or complementary objects, for their common gratification. Being inveterate travellers, they decided as well to choose objects typical of the places they visited together. At present they are in Castroville, self-styled "artichoke capital of the world", examining in their motel bedroom the many varieties and attributes of that vegetable, confident that between stem and heart they will soon meet this new challenge to their ingenious pursuit of happiness.

As her plane rises from the pot-holed airstrip at Mtabe, masturbating invisibly but vigorously, with both hands thrust through the slit pockets of her djellabah, a fifty-one-year-old reporter sits chatting with her neighbour. In thirty years of globe-trotting, masturbation has remained a talisman against the terrors of take-off and landing, one by now virtually automatic, yet still effective.

Two men lying in bed, one in his forties, the other thirty-three. The younger masturbating, almost desperately, straining for climax; the other encouraging him with gentle words, stroking his shoulder, only when the other struggles into ultimate pleasure leaning over to slip his tongue between the gasping lips. Scene: somewhere in Tehran.

A twenty-four-year-old cellist is sitting naked on a stool in her bedroom in Manila. Her legs are spread; her left hand pulls back the folds of her vulva; her right hand is drawing the tip of a cello bow over her clitoris in fluttering tremolo.

Inmates of the pensioners home in Constantia, Romania, four women (aged seventy-one, seventy-three, seventy-four and seventy-six) and four men (seventy, seventy-two, seventy-five, seventy-eight) conceive and execute a plan for independent, simultaneous masturbation. Each agrees to aim for orgasm, in the privacy of bed, on the twelfth stroke of midnight every Saturday night, after the weekly bingo and dancing. — The director of the home will later be struck by the particular vivacity of these eight as it grows from week to week. They will refuse, however, to divulge the reason for their zest.

Dropping a silver dollar in the slot of a steel-and-chrome cabinet resembling a cigarette dispenser and standing against one wall of a Honolulu brothel, a sailor of fifty-nine introduces his half-tumescent penis into a rubber-edged opening at the centre of the machine, which starts humming and whirring with muted rotations.

After sixty-two years, a highly educated woman of Karachi has retained two passions: masturbation and the singing of Maria Callas. She is now indulging both of them, rolling on six thicknesses of Bakhtiari rug to the strains of a pirated *Fedora*. The music — that voice — do not augment her sexual pleasure: they frustrate and delay it. Sometimes two hours will pass in incompatible ecstasies before they come to a necessary end.

In Perth, Australia, a twenty-six-year-old woman is masturbating as she squats above the face of a seventy-nine-year-old man; he is lying on his back and also masturbating. His penis is not quite erect. The woman is urging him to take all the time he needs.

A quasi-subversive organisation founded recently in Prague encourages its members to invent obstacles to overcome while masturbating. The organisation is called Masturbation and Its Discontents — MAID for short. The first task set by the English chapter is to complete masturbation while reciting Milton's "Il Penseroso" to no less than three listeners. The feat is first accomplished in Durham by a male, aged fifty-seven, who ejaculates at the line "While the bee with honied thigh".

A member of MAID in Bangkok, a woman of sixty-seven, becomes the first to reach orgasm under the dentist's drill.

When a racing driver belonging to MAID attempts masturbation during the running of the Long Beach *grand prix*, the Prague office bans all tests involving physical risk (the team skydiving experiment at Châlon-sur-Saône is promptly cancelled) and declares a week's moratorium to commemorate the victim of the crash, dead at thirty-six.

At the age of forty-two, a male member of the Tiflis chapter of MAID undertakes to masturbate when he goes jogging in the outlying hills. His plan is aborted by a compassionate shepherdess who brings it to a conclusion of her own choosing. Although protesting his innocence, the man is expelled from MAID at once. He marries the shepherdess three weeks later.

A man of sixty-three belonging to the Toronto chapter of MAID successfully masturbates in a slaughterhouse while steers are being killed and disembowelled. His achievement is not recognised after it is discovered that people of both sexes bribe their way into the slaughterhouse every day to perform this very act.

Not far from Limerick, in a dank twilit field, a girl of ten is sitting on the dappled hindquarters of a recumbent cow, pulling its tail tight between her thighs — warm bristle and bone against her warm wet bone.

An anthropologist approaches a seventeen-year-old male standing on a beach near Suva, in the Fijis, and unselfconsciously masturbating into mild Pacific surf. He asks the boy the name for what he is doing. "*Tokolano*", answers the youth, which means: "keeping the moon under".

Much time in her forty-six years has been devoted to sexual investigation, but she is struck with novel pleasure when, in Colombo, she enters the ship-chandler's warehouse. She comes back late that afternoon, hides until closing time, and spends the night masturbating again and again to the touch of hawsers, mooring rings, anchor chains — the hardy gear of seagoing men. Tomorrow she will buy cordage for home use.

Husband-and-wife contortionists from the Cirque d'Hiver are demonstrating their masturbatory prowess to a private party of businesspersons in São Paulo. Initial excitement (their mouths touch every inch of their bodies) and admiration for their comeliness (they look half their respective forty-one and forty years) ultimately give way to melancholy and regret, for who could help wanting such gifts for oneself?

Twenty miles east of Kabul, in total darkness, a forty-four-year-old peasant stealthily performs a time-honoured rite. At the centre of his field, with the butt of his hoe, he has worked a small hole in the clayey earth. Now, kneading his penis into workable tumescence, he lies face down and buries it in the hole, poking hard so that the cold will not shrivel him. Nearby rocket salvos precipitate orgasm before he can complete his whispered incantation.

Cruising at twenty-eight thousand feet somewhere between Wake and Marcus Islands, a jetliner suddenly plunges out of control. Sitting by a window inside the plane, a woman of forty-three glances hurriedly at her neighbour: he is convulsed with terror. "Have to look after myself," she sighs, quickly loosening her slacks and slipping one hand to the point of her vulva. Her climax occurs as the plane pulls out at two thousand feet. Her shout of pleasure is lost in the hubbub.

In a Beirut residence a woman asks her forty-nine-year-old lover to masturbate on to her. He emerges from her, straddles her hips, and soon flakes of semen flutter down on her belly and breasts.

A girl of fourteen is using a small, still-wriggling, mackerel-shaped fish to penetrate her barely mature vagina, seated on a beach near Datumakuta, in eastern Borneo. This is a ritual among her people — mothers, grandmothers, and seventeen aunts look on approvingly.

A tourist lies on a bed in a Barcelona brothel masturbating. He is watching a handsome young woman hurriedly taking off her clothes and jewels. "*Espera!*" she implores, but he does not want to wait. Entering the place almost by accident, he has discovered in this woman the embodiment of his dearest fantasies. (He is twenty-seven, she a year or two older.) He wants to masturbate while looking at her palpable self as he has so often done imagining her. But she is too quick for him. Kicking away her shoes, seizing his wrists, she settles stockinged thighs about his member in the very nick so that, bursting inside her, he feels something beyond pleasure, regret, desire — a flashing blackness that leaves him unconscious as she, with a compassionate laugh, gathers him in her arms.

A twenty-eight-year-old woman is masturbating in a drab bedroom on the outskirts of Singapore. She is sitting on a cot in front of her husband, who has just ejaculated in her. The man watches her unconcernedly. As she starts to come he bends down and rolls his tongue inside her cunt. She shrieks.

The world's greatest masturbator, who lives in Budapest, is masturbating as he does every workday evening as soon as he gets home. He lives in a large apartment — he is a member of the Politburo of the Hungarian Communist Party. He is also, at sixty-five, a man of robust health and sanguine humour. At the end of yet another hard day's work, he has gone straight to his study and rolled back a large plain rug, disclosing a twenty-foot-square map of the world underneath. At the centre of the map is Hungary; or more precisely, Budapest; and even more precisely, himself — there he stands, watching his sperm as it splatters the planisphere, laughing gleefully as he thinks of the Hungarians who are almost sure to be found wherever his seed has fallen: Hungarians who at this very moment are taking over laboratories, universities, businesses, banks. . . Today, Budapest; tomorrow, the world! And it will be a better world.

A fifteen-year-old girl is swimming near Tenerife. Straddling a sunken mooring rope, she is pulling herself along it, back and forth. Her pleasure is slow in coming. When it does, she senses the chill that has entered her flesh from the cool water.

Sitting on an overstuffed chair by his bed, a boy of nine is masturbating near Stamford, Connecticut. He does not ejaculate, but a pearl of sperm gathers at the point of his still-childish erection. He knows what's going on.

1981

THE ORCHARD

Foreword

When Georges Perec died in March, 1982, he was famous in his own country, with hundreds of friends and thousands of admirers. He was known chiefly for his books — his first novel, *Les Choses*, won the Prix Renaudot in 1966, his monumental *La Vie mode d'emploi* the Prix Médicis in 1978 — but he was also familiar to many through his weekly crossword puzzles in *Le Point* and his intermittent appearances on radio and television. No one who came in contact with him ever forgot him. His untimely death at 46 as a result of lung cancer came as a scarcely credible shock.

In the early seventies I had told Georges Perec about Joe Brainard's *I Remember* series, in which the American writer, already distinguished as an artist, had demonstrated a new and altogether seductive approach to autobiography. My account proved somewhat inexact: my inaccuracy can be forgiven in that it led Perec to begin his own *Je me souviens* (published in 1978), a less intimate but no less enthralling work than Brainard's.

Shortly after Perec's death, I adopted the "I remember" mode to write about him. I did so neither to pay homage to him nor to salvage our years of friendship, simply to avail myself of the written word in facing the dismay that at that moment was overwhelming so many of us. Every day for several months I wrote down one or two recollections in the form of "I remember Georges Perec", without trying to be exhaustive or particularly acute: I accepted all the items that occurred to me as though they were pebbles cast ashore by a rough sea, to be pondered and assigned their place. I cannot call the experience a consoling or liberating one, but at least I was able to name one by one the fragments of the pathetic tumulus that I was assembling.

One day I forgot to set down my memories. Soon after that I gave up the practice for good. Much later, I reviewed these pages so as to provide them with an order more appropriate to their subject, that is, a less arbitrary one. Even so, they cannot amount to more than a sadly occasional sequence, composed in fits and starts, finally leading nowhere.

Paris, September, 1987

I remember sometimes arranging to meet Georges Perec on the bus or the *métro*. He always sat by a window, and I recognised him from far away — his Afro hair and his goatee gave his face the projective power of a primitive mask.

I remember being told before I knew him that Georges Perec liked a good laugh. The man I met was full of despair; but at social gatherings he would make pun after pun, nervously, almost compulsively. His "good laugh" was a kind way of keeping others at a distance.

I remember being irritated when, after Georges Perec died, people asked if he smoked a lot. His death was plainly too enormous to be attributed to anything so commonplace. Later, his doctors told Catherine B. that the tumour in his lungs had nothing to do with tobacco; later still, I learned that his cancer was typical of heavy smokers.

I remember asking Georges Perec, who had been a bicycle-racing fan, why it was so much easier to maintain speed when following another cyclist. Was the explanation mechanical, psychological, or both? He answered that there was nothing to explain — either I understood or I didn't.

I remember arriving with Georges Perec at Gare d'Austerlitz in the summer of 1975. Although on the lookout for Catherine B., he failed to see her where she stood solitary and beautiful at the end of the platform; I had to point her out to him.

I remember Georges Perec on the beach at Ile de Ré. Because his pale skin burned easily, he wore a hooded white-cotton burnous — he looked like an oil sheikh. (On a trip to the Seychelles, he was seared painfully.)

I remember asking Georges Perec not to tell me about *"53 jours"** while he was working on it. I wanted the finished book to be a complete surprise.

I remember being startled by Georges Perec's harsh judgements of those he no longer liked. At a gallery opening he referred to O.O. as a fink. Others so treated were N.W., I.Y.

I remember discussing with Georges Perec the virtues of various disposable razors. When I switched to Gillette's new double-bladed model, he happily acquired the stock of Wilkinsons that I had amassed during the preceding months.

I remember drinking 1929 Château Canon with Georges Perec at a restaurant near my apartment, where we had been working together one rainy winter Sunday. The Château Canon cost one hundred and thirty francs. Georges said that he had never paid that much for a bottle of wine and never would. Through a comparison with the age and price of other Bordeaux on the list, I convinced him that this was a bargain. We drank two bottles.

I remember eating dinner with Georges Perec at the Balzar, Chez Marcel (rue Saint-Nicolas), La Fontaine aux Carmes, Le Petit Robert, Benoît, Le Vaudeville, Le Train Bleu, L'Épi d'Or, Marty, Chez Yvonne, Au Buisson Ardent, Les Fleurs, Le Terminus Nord, Julien, Le Pavillon du Lac, Sel et Poivre, Le Palmier de Zinc, Beckett, at Dédé's on rue Linné and at another tiny place across the street, the *brasserie* of La Closerie des Lilas, Le Pactol, La Gauloise, Tan Dinh, L'Alsace à Paris, La Chope d'Orsay, Chez Gérard.

I remember Georges Perec pretending not to be Georges Perec when a young woman approached him during a lunch in Orsay. He was irritated at being recognised. Some time later, he and I were having coffee in the *brasserie* of a supermarket outside Grenoble when a waitress politely asked him if he wasn't Georges Perec. With neither pleasure nor displeasure he admitted he was. I asked him how often this happened. "Several times a week." He added that his picture appeared in each issue of *Le Point*, he had had a lot of exposure on television lately, and his face was not easily forgotten.

I remember Georges Perec expressing his appreciation of the towelling called Essuitout: *"Ça essuie vraiment tout!"* *

I remember requesting that the first meeting of the Oulipo after Georges Perec's death begin by his being unanimously reprimanded for abandoning us so inexcusably.

I remember disagreeing with Georges Perec about movies — *Putney Swope* (*"Mais c'est une merde!"*)*, *Avanti!* (*"Mais c'est fantastique!"*), perhaps Truffaut in general.

I remember driving Georges Perec past the slope in Villard-de-Lans where he skied as a boy — was it Les Bains, or the one farther down the road he lived on?

I remember eating out with Georges Perec in La Balme-de-Rencurel; at a roadside restaurant near the Albany airport; in Orsay several times during the week the Oulipo spent there; in Bennington; in Grenoble; in Chambéry; in Saulieu.

I remember Georges Perec at our last lunch asking me not to smoke. He had given up smoking a few days before, and he was anxious to avoid temptation.

I remember Georges Perec grinning madly as he danced a furious jerk with Catherine B. in Andy Warhol's apartment, which Renaud C. had borrowed for a big party. After working up a tremendous sweat, Georges Perec asked to take a shower. He soon reappeared among us with only a towel around his waist. He was irresistible.

I remember Georges Perec's admiration for Robert Scipion. When asked about crossword puzzles, he invariably gave as the exemplar of a crossword definition Scipion's *faire du vieux avec du neuf (nonagénaire).*

I remember finding with Georges Perec the house where he had lived in Villard-de-Lans (on the road leading east out of town, on the left, just before the entrance to La Moraine) and being unable to find the house where he had lived in Lans-en-Vercors.

I remember Georges Perec's bad teeth. They deteriorated unchecked during the years when he disliked himself. In 1975 he began going to a dentist (a woman, I think) to have them mended, a laborious process that he willingly endured.

I remember Georges Perec drinking five neat glasses of Wyborowka at our first meeting at the Bar du Pont-Royal. I kept him company. We went to the Chope d'Orsay for dinner and got even drunker on wine.

I remember meeting Georges Perec in the Chope d'Orsay the following year. We were at different tables (he may have been dining with Jacques L.). When he came over, he pulled up his left sleeve to reveal two parallel razor cuts. He looked like a schoolboy showing a bad report card to his parents.

I remember feeling jealous whenever Georges Perec told me he was busy dining with someone else: *"C'est un copain,"** he would say, mentioning a name unknown to me. (I told him about all my friends.) I wondered if I was a *copain*, or only *l'ami américain?*

I remember Georges Perec calling me in Lans to tell me, with punctilious calm, that Queneau had died. Tears came afterwards. We had lost the man who authorised our lives as writers — a trustworthy, irreplaceable father. I later learned that each of us that evening re-read Queneau's poems about death, the very ones we had read out loud to each other a few weeks before.

I remember Georges Perec shovelling snow in the yard at Lans, although just long enough for M.C. to photograph him.

I remember Georges Perec drinking Château Lapelleterie at the Balzar and Beaune Grèves "Vignes de l'enfant Jésus" at Marty.

I remember Georges Perec saying *"C'est chiant comme la mort."**

I remember Georges Perec's bald spot, like an outcropping of rock in a dense forest.

I remember Georges Perec scratching his goatee.

I remember Georges Perec's enthusiasm when I did good work writing in French and his gentle suggestions to abandon work that was of doubtful quality.

I remember Georges Perec's infinite tolerance for work animated by some sense of beauty and his impatience with work lacking that sense, no matter how "interesting". He had no patience with Janácek.

I remember Georges Perec giving up cigarettes for less harmful cigarillos. When asked if he inhaled the cigarillos, he replied, "No more than I have to."

I remember Georges Perec saying that buttered French bread *(une tartine beurrée)* was the most delectable food in the world. His usual breakfast consisted of a *tartine* and *café au lait*.

I remember Georges Perec's eyes: brown, big, beautiful.

I remember Georges Perec telling me that once on a radio broadcast he vaunted the largest Mont Blanc fountain pen at considerable length in the hope that the manufacturer would send him one.

I remember Georges Perec deducing that *Tlooth* had been constructed around a secret verbal palindrome. He found convincing evidence for this, including the exchange of *m* and *n* in the words *atonic bomb* and *formication* — something I had done unintentionally.

I remember Georges Perec's unqualified love of novels that embodied a far-reaching vision — *The Magic Mountain, Doktor Faustus, Under the Volcano*. He never questioned my reservations about them but only emphasised their scope once again, so eloquently that I wanted to reread them at once.

I remember Georges Perec teaching me charades and rebuses (such as *anchois pommier* and *au s... au s... au secours...*).* For him schoolboy silliness was the beginning of laughter.

I remember Georges Perec's excitement when I told him that a pinch of snuff would satisfy his nicotine craving for half an hour, and his disappointment when this proved false. He continued to take snuff all the same, sneezing and snorting with long "aahs" of contentment.

I remember Georges Perec telling me, after an Oulipo meeting, that in speaking to the group I used *n'est-ce pas?* so often that it could not fail to distract or annoy.

I remember Georges Perec's laughs — the first high, fast, and anxious; the second even higher and faster, full of delighted astonishment; the third a low, satisfied chuckle that was reserved for intimate company. When he smiled, his eyes shone.

I remember going to the theatre with Georges Perec: 1. To a play by Feydeau, with Catherine B. (M.C., whom I had just met, joined us for supper afterwards.) 2. *La Belle Hélène*, with M.C. and Catherine B. (At one point the actors gave the audience a quiz. To the question "Who was the second oldest Greek poet whose works have survived?" I correctly shouted the answer "Hesiod", then, to the delight of Georges and Catherine, squirmed down into my seat like an embarrassed little boy.) 3. *La Plage* (by Severo Sarduy), with M.C. and Catherine B. (It was wet weather, Georges and Catherine had bad colds, they arrived at Gare d'Orsay at the last possible moment with grey, swollen faces.)

I remember a card thumbtacked outside Georges Perec's front door, with "Georges Perec" printed in large lettering, followed by information in smaller print that referred to a housepainter living in another part of Paris.

I remember that one might also find on Georges Perec's door a piece of paper with the handwritten words *Je reviens de Suisse.**

I remember lying to Georges Perec when we first met: *"Je n'ai lu de toi que* Les Choses."** I had read nothing by him at all.

I remember Georges Perec's impatience with certain subjects during the time he was writing *La Vie mode d'emploi*: *"Qu'est-ce que cela peut bien me foutre?"**

I remember Georges Perec's sinus headaches.

I remember how exuberantly pleased Georges Perec was with the gift of a carving board that M.C. and I had bought at the Beaucroissant fair: he repeated, *"Ah, que je suis content que vous me donniez cette planche!"* (Or *"d'avoir cette planche de vous".*)*

I remember making Georges Perec one of my literary executors (the other was Maxine G.).

I remember that Georges Perec always got to the train station at least an hour before departure time.

I remember George Perec's sneezing fits.

I remember taking Georges Perec to Le Clocher, the Catholic boarding-school in Villard-de-Lans where he had been hidden (and incidentally baptised, with a false name) during the occupation. The director asked him, "You wouldn't by any chance be a relative of the writer?" Hunching his shoulders, Georges answered, "I *am* the writer." *Les Choses* was now being taught there.

I remember Georges Perec's warts.

I remember Georges Perec sulky and silent while he was writing *La Vie mode d'emploi.*

I remember my daughter telling me that she had seen Georges Perec at a party and found him greatly aged.

I remember speaking to Georges Perec about *Raiders of the Lost Ark* as soon as the film was released. I was sure he would like it, the way schoolboys like adventure movies they play hookey for. We saw it in a big movie theatre on the Champs-Elysées, without our ladies, and (most important) at a matinee.

I remember that Georges Perec always named his current cat Duchat.* (A few days before he died, the last Duchat turned against him, clawing him several times while he lay in bed.)

I remember Georges Perec telling me that Calvados was the most reliable of commercially produced spirits. (His favourite brandies were *prune de Souillac* and rare Armagnacs.)

I remember going home after dinner with Georges Perec to smoke dope and listen to classical music — big works like the Brahms *Requiem* — during which we would lie on the living-room rug, rolling with pleasure at the climaxes. At such times I wanted to take him in my arms.

I remember Georges Perec walking through the cold in his sheepskin jacket, head forward, shoulders hunched.

I remember Georges Perec's admiration of the waiters at the Balzar: *"Nulle part on est aussi bien servi."* *

I remember my last meal with Georges Perec, on the day I was leaving for New York: lunch at the Bar du Pont-Royal, where we had met twelve years before.

I remember that before 1975 expressions such as *dans ce bas monde* and *dans ce val de larmes** figured frequently (if ironically) in Georges Perec's conversation; after that date, never.

I remember that Georges Perec and I disagreed about *Under the Volcano*, about Tolstoy's novels, about Thomas Mann, about *Peanuts*.

I remember that at our first dinner after the completion of his analysis Georges Perec told me that now, when he walked down the street to mail a letter at the post office, he knew he was walking down the street to mail a letter at the post office.

I remember seeing Georges Perec lying in his coffin in the hospital morgue: his face was narrow and grave, his mouth was shut in an unnatural fashion (as though the lips had been sewn together to keep the jaw from sagging), his hair had been brushed close to his skull (what undertaker could have imagined his Afro?). Catherine B. said, "*Mais ce n'est pas lui!*"* and ran her fingers through his hair to fluff it up.

I remember Georges Perec working on trains on his crossword puzzles for *Le Point*, on an Oulipian exercise, on a poem that was also an Oulipian exercise.

I remember that Georges Perec gave a huge party every year on his birthday, although I only went once or twice. I best remember the evening when Agnes Q. threw a glass of wine at me, Stella B. made her mocking, bull's-eye remark ("*Harry, je ne savais pas que tu étais féministe!*")* and, elsewhere and later, I struggled to move the virtually passed-out T. into her bedroom, gashing my knee on a glass table in my effort, only to discover that we had been in her bedroom all the while.

I remember Georges Perec had two friends called invariably by their last names: Gautier (Henri), Guitaut (Jacqueline).

I remember that Georges Perec had no aesthetic prejudices.

I remember telling Georges Perec over dinner that I had had an affair with T. two years before. He said that if he had known at the time he would have been offended, that he couldn't care less now (he was too happy with Catherine B.).

I remember that Georges Perec did not mind eating in the new *gril express* on French trains because they offered an acceptable smoked seafood platter that could be washed down with vodka.

I remember staying up most of the night helping Georges Perec and Catherine B. finish editing *Les Lieux d'une fugue.** We ate dinner twice in the same restaurant, near the Pied de Cochon, once at 8 p.m., once at 4 a.m., when all was truly finished.

I remember that in the course of an evening at Nicole B.'s, when I went on babbling during a televised performance of *Don Carlos*, Georges Perec reached over several intervening bodies to slap the top of my head with the words, "*Tais-toi, l'américain!*" *

I remember Georges Perec getting off the bus at Trocadéro and ostentatiously dropping his ticket on the middle of the sidewalk, smiling as he did so. I still cannot see his point.

I remember that Georges Perec had a deliberately "shy" way of looking at you — eyes wide open, lips pressed together, head tilted to the right, and, sometimes, hands touching by the fingertips — that recalled a photograph taken of him in the '60's and another, with his mother, taken when he was a little boy.

I remember that Georges Perec knew everything about serious *bandes dessinées* * and that I never saw him reading a *B.D.* book. I rarely saw him reading any book.

I remember M. reporting that when she told Georges Perec that I would never go to bed with a girl friend of his, he replied, "But he already has!" I still don't know whom he meant (this was before my affair with T.) — perhaps H.W.?

I remember my surprise when I read Georges Perec's statement that as a writer he was a child of the Oulipo and only a distant cousin of Raymond Queneau.

I remember Georges Perec and Laurent de B. waiting for me when I landed by ferry at Ile de Ré.

I remember that Georges Perec loved *Peanuts* and that he had learned from it most of the English he knew when he began translating *Tlooth*.

I remember that Georges Perec never repeated himself.

I remember that Georges Perec detested champagne when I met him and loved it during his last years.

I remember that Georges Perec never ate vegetables — he halfheartedly attributed his dislike of them to institutional cooking in his childhood — and loved fresh pasta.

I remember Suzon. I remember Barbara K. I remember Catherine T. (I introduced her to him, a fiasco ensued, with resentment on both sides.) I remember the young woman he stopped seeing because he was appalled by his use of her: *"Je l'appelle, elle vient, je me vide en elle, je ne la revois plus jusqu'à la prochaine fois."**

I remember that Georges Perec was a socialist.

I remember that Georges Perec was enthusiastic over my first account of the e s t Training and that he later spoke of it with mistrust.

I remember that Georges Perec, without seeming to keep up to date in his reading, knew everything about current writing.

I remember that Georges Perec taught me the expressions *se faire couler un bronze* and *avoir le pain d'épices au bord des lèvres.**

I remember that Georges Perec wanted to establish the name *un matiouze* ("a Mathews") for the strong espresso I always ordered, using M.'s formula "a double espresso in a demitasse." In restaurants he would order *un matiouze*, then explain the term, hoping it would catch on — an impossible hope.

I remember that, of all the forms imagination can take, memory is usually the most inert.

I remember that Georges Perec wore rounded shoes, often thick-soled, never tapered, never shinable, never ugly. They manifested his achieved desire to be firmly present in every situation.

I remember that Georges Perec was pleased by the prospect of including the phrase *ses tunnels* in *"53 jours"* to satisfy Jeff G., a New Zealander who was constructing a ten-by-ten word square from published sources and needed this item to complete it.

I remember that Georges Perec had little interest in having authors sign their books for him or in signing his own books for others. What mattered was the book itself.

I remember that Georges Perec often praised something that he particularly liked, such as a delicious wine, as *un don des dieux*.* (Occasionally he said *"C'est sublime,"* perhaps in friendly use of an expression I overworked.)

I remember that Georges Perec wore graceful white and off-white Indian shirts, loose and hanging outside his trousers.

I remember that Georges Perec was never sick, except for *la crève* (*"Comment vas-tu?"* *"J'ai la crève"*)* — a kind of flu that subsumed head cold, sinus trouble and hangover.

I remember that on the evening of September 11, 1982, Émilie C., aged 13, called out, "There's someone talking on the radio who sounds exactly like Georges Perec!" We rushed into the living-room and listened to a rebroadcast of one of Jacques B.'s series called "Fifty things I'd like to do before I die." Georges had restricted himself to thirty-seven — still far too many, as it turned out.

I remember that during the summer I had a Eurail card, Georges Perec was disappointed that rather than simply using it to go where I needed, I didn't keep travelling back and forth between Oslo and Seville.

I remember two pranks of which Georges Perec never tired. I. Pointing to shirt front: *"T'as une tache."* * Bringing up finger to catch victim's lowered nose: *"Moustache!"* 2. Seated in a car, following the slamming of one of its doors with an agonised *"Aïe!"*

I remember that Georges Perec would settle on a Bordeaux to drink whenever he ate at the Balzar — Château Lapelleterie during one period, Bordeaux *réserve* during the last.

I remember, over one of our last meals, Georges Perec expressing his sadness at not having a family. For one thing, he would never inherit anything. I promised to include him in my will if that was any consolation.

I remember that whenever I watched Georges Perec at work, I was struck by his sureness: he never hesitated in the choice of a word or the shaping of a sentence.

I remember that when I first met Georges Perec he had "problems with women". He dreamed of a beautiful, intelligent and successful woman who in the midst of far-flung travels would from time to time suddenly appear at his door, offer her absolute love, and then leave.

I remember that when my father died, what made the loss bearable was having Georges Perec in my life.

I remember seeing three exceptional movies thanks to Georges Perec: *Reflections in a Golden Eye* (in the sepia version), *Solaris,* and the Robert Altman film that takes place in the Houston Astrodome.

I remember that when I was driving with Georges Perec in the United States, he read all the road signs out loud, incorporating them into his knowledge of English immediately and permanently.

I remember that on the day M. returned to America for good, Georges Perec and I drank a bottle of 1961 Clos Saint Denis, a wine M. loved, in the huge Baccarat glasses she had given me for my birthday.

I remember that when he was alone Georges Perec skipped lunch.

I remember Georges Perec reminding me of a faun, a dormouse, or a new-born bear cub.

I remember that when I suggested that, in the case of objects, *apporter* was preferable to *amener,* Georges Perec declared, *"Je conchie la langue française."* *

I also remember Georges Perec admonishing Raymond Queneau for saying *basé sur* instead of *fondé sur*.*

I remember experiencing great happiness on the day in June, 1975, when I realised I loved Georges Perec without reservation.

I remember that at a Boulez concert-lecture Georges Perec rattled off a list of imaginary composers whose names combined the classical and the modern. I can recall only Hector Berio.

I remember waking up eleven days after Georges Perec died and realising that I was turning the remembrance of his death into the conviction that every day is ruined before it begins — a convenient "waking anguish" I had given up seven years before.

I remember, about the same time, thinking that people I passed in the streets of Paris all looked as though they were mourning Georges Perec.

I remember wondering how Georges Perec, who never seemed to read a newspaper, was so well informed about current events.

I remember, the day after Georges Perec died, wanting to convey what had happened to my American students. I had spoken of him earlier in the course; I now began a lengthier account of him, noting on the blackboard "Georges Perec (1936–   )", detailing his achievements and accomplishments for a quarter of an hour, only then announcing his death and completing the parenthesis.

I remember worrying about having Georges Perec meet my mother. He was less than partial to well-to-do genteel ladies; she firmly disapproved of men without jackets and ties. But both were full of warmth and enthusiasm, each knew how much I loved the other. I wish they had met.

I remember that Georges Perec loved to ski.

I remember that in the course of my last telephone conversation with Georges Perec (he was in Paris, I in New York) he told me that he had a tumour in his lung for which he was to undergo surgery six weeks later; he asked if he could stay with us for part of his convalescence. After the hospital, after another month with the family of Catherine B., he arrived in Lans-en-Vercors on May 13th, just as the orchard was coming into blossom. He was extremely pale; it was hard for me to get used to his crew cut and missing beard (he meant his appearance to show unequivocally that he had started a new life); but the mountain air quickly revived him, his face took on colour, and his step grew stronger. I remember Georges Perec at the end of a short outing standing somewhat out of breath amid the lengthening grass of the hillside, leaning against a plum tree, smiling contentedly as he conversed with his visitors, old friends who had travelled a long way to see him — Anton Voyl; the painter Valène; Jérôme and Sylvie, a couple he had known for many years of whom he was particularly fond.*

1982

Notes

carving board from you).

79 *Duchat:* McCat.

Nulle part on est aussi bien servi: Nowhere else is the service so good.

80 *dans ce bas monde:* in this vile world.

dans ce val de larmes: in this vale of tears.

Mais ce n'est pas lui: But that's not him at all.

81 *je ne savais pas que tu étais féministe:* I didn't know you were a women's libber.

Les Lieux d'une fugue: A film written and directed by Perec.

82 *Tais-toi:* Shut up.

bandes dessinées (B. D.): Comic books, often written with serious intent for adults.

83 *Je l'appelle . . . jusqu'à la prochaine fois:* I call her up, she comes over, I pour myself into her, I don't see her again until the next time around.

84 *se faire couler un bronze:* To cast some bronze (to defecate).

avoir le pain d'épices au bord des lèvres: To be bursting with gingerbread (to be on the verge of defecating).

85 *un don des dieux:* a gift of the gods.

Comment vas-tu? J'ai la crève: How are you? I'm at death's door.

86 *T'as une tache:* You made a spot (*moustache* rhymes emphatically with *tache*).

Aïe: Ouch.

87 *apporter, amener:* to bring.

Je conchie la langue française: I shit on the French language.

88 *basé sur, fondé sur:* based on.

89 *Anton Voyl; Valène; Jérôme and Sylvie:* characters in Perec's novels *La Disparition, La Vie mode d'emploi, Les Choses.*

Translation and the Oulipo: The Case of the Persevering Maltese

These pages were first presented at the French Institute in London in October, 1996, as the third of the St. Jerome lectures, a series devoted to the topic of translation.

The word "Oulipo" is the acronym of the Ouvroir de littérature potentielle, *or "workshop for potential literature", a group founded in 1960 by Raymond Queneau and François Le Lionnais. The group was created to explore what becomes possible when writing is subjected to arbitrary and restrictive procedures, preferably definable in mathematical terms. Since many have found this undertaking preposterous, it seemed useful to turn to translation and its attendant problems in making the interest of Oulipian methods clearer to sceptical writers and readers, as well as in examining the Case of the Persevering Maltese.*

A Problem in Translation

Some of you may know the name of Ernest Botherby (born in Perth, Australia, 1869; died in Adelaide, 1944), the scholar who founded the Australian school of ethno-linguistics, and also the explorer who identified the variety of *Apegetes* known as *botherbyi*, popular in England during the years before the Great War when private greenhouses were still common. Botherby attained professional notoriety in the late '20s, after publishing several papers on a language from New Guinea called Pagolak. The peoples of New Guinea were a favourite subject with Botherby. He had begun studying them years before when, at the age of twenty-four, he undertook a solitary voyage into the interior of the island, vast areas of which remained uncharted at the time. A collation of reports by Nicholas von Mikhucho Maclay, the Reverend Macfarlane, and Otto Finsch had convinced young Botherby that tribes still existed in the highlands of New Guinea that had shunned contact with their neighbours, not to mention the modern world, and preserved a truly primitive culture.

Starting from Tagota at the mouth of the Fly, Botherby traversed the river by steam launch to a point over five hundred miles inland, whence he proceeded in more modest craft almost to its headwaters. After establishing a base camp, he travelled across the plains into the mountain forests, finally arriving at the unexplored region he was looking for, a complex of valleys lying — to use the toponymy of the time — between the Kaiserin Augusta, the Victor Emmanuel Mountains, and the continuation of the Musgrave Range.

In one of these valleys Botherby discovered, as he had hoped, his first archaic tribe. He designates it as that of the Ohos. This community, numbering no more than a few hundred, lived a peaceable existence in conditions of extreme simplicity. Its members were hunter-gatherers equipped with rudimentary tools. They procured fire from conflagrations occurring in forests nearby but were incapable of making it otherwise. They also used speech, but a speech reduced to its minimum. The Oho language consisted of only three words and one expression, the invariable statement, "Red makes wrong." Having patiently won over the tribal chiefs, Botherby was able to verify this fact during the many weeks he spent with them. Other needs and wishes were communicated by sounds and signs; actual words were never used except for this unique assertion that "Red makes wrong."

In time Botherby signified to his hosts a curiosity as to whether other communities existed in the region. The Ohos pointed north and east. When Botherby pointed west, he met with fierce disapproval. So it was naturally west that he next went, prudently distancing himself from the Oho settlement before taking that direction. His hunch was rewarded two days later when, in another valley, he came upon his second tribe, which he called the Uhas. The Uhas lived in a manner much like the Ohos, although they knew how to cultivate several edible roots and had domesticated the native pig; like the Ohos, they had a rudimentary language used invariably to make a single statement. The Uhas' statement was, "Here not there." They used it as exclusively as the Ohos used "Red makes wrong."

Botherby eventually made his way back to the valley of the Ohos. There he was overcome by an understandable (if professionally incorrect) eagerness to share his second discovery, to wit, that near them lived a people of the same stock, leading a similar life, and possessed of the same basic gift of speech. As he was expounding this information with gestures that his audience readily understood, Botherby reached the point where he plainly needed to transmit the gist of the Uhas' one statement. He hesitated. How do you render "Here not there" in a tongue that can only express "Red makes wrong"?

Botherby did not hesitate long. He saw, as you of course see, that he had no choice. There was only one solution. He grasped at once what all translators eventually learn: a language says what it can say, and that's that.

Yes, but we're different

The range of the Oho and Uha languages is tiny; the range of modern languages — for instance, French and English — is vast. There is virtually nothing that can be said in English that cannot be said in French, and vice versa. Information, like phone numbers and race results, can easily be swapped between the two languages. Then again, some statements that seem informative do not really pass.

A Frenchman says, *"Je suis français"*; an American says, "I'm American." "I'm French" and *"Je suis américain"* strike us as accurate translations. But are they? A Frenchman who asserts that he is French invokes willy-nilly a communal past of social, cultural, even conceptual evolution, one that transcends the mere legality of citizenship. But the fact of citizenship is what is paramount to most Americans, who probably feel, rightly or wrongly, that history is theirs to invent. The two national identities are radically different, and claims to them cannot be usefully translated in a way that will bridge this gap.

I suggest that this gap extends into the remotest corners of the two languages. *Elle s'est levée de bonne heure* means "She arose early", but in expectation of different breakfasts and waking from dreams in another guise. This does not mean that it's wrong to translate plain statements in a plain way, only that it is worth remembering that such translations tell us what writers say and not who they are. In this respect, French and English — or Germans and Portuguese — would seem to be as separate as Ohos and Uhas.

There are also times when plain statements of fact do translate each other rather well — even the statements *Je suis français* and *I'm American.* To make what I mean clear, let me add to them one or two supplementary words. The Frenchman says, "*Je suis français, Monsieur!*" The American says, "I'm American, and you better believe it!" You see at once that the meaning of both statements is the same: an assertion not of nationality but of committed membership in a community — "my community." So even essentials can sometimes break through the linguistic separation.

What makes this interesting is that the substantial identity of these statements does not lie in what they say — the information they contain is obviously not identical (French/American). So in this instance, at any rate, what has been successfully translated lies not in the nominal sense of the words but in other factors of language, whatever they may be. And whatever they may be, these factors are precisely the material of Oulipian experiment.

So can the Oulipo help translators in their delicate task?

Translation and the Oulipo (1)

The Oulipo certainly can't help in an obvious way. Unless he wanted to sabotage his employer, an editor would be mad to employ an Oulipian as a translator.

A few samples will show why. As our source text, let's take a famous line from Racine's *Phèdre*:

> *C'est Vénus tout entière à sa proie attachée.*

The literal sense — please be charitable — is, "Here is Venus steadfastly fastened to her prey."

First translation: "I saw Alice jump highest — I, on silly crutches".

Explanation: a rule of measure has been applied to the original. Each of its words is replaced by another word having the same number of letters.

Second translation: "Don't tell anyone what we've learned until you're out in the street. Then shout it out, and when that one-horse carriage passes by, create a general pandemonium." Explanation: the sound of the original has been imitated as closely as possible — *C'est Vénus tout entière à sa proie attachée* / Save our news, toot, and share as uproar at a shay — and the results expanded into a narrative fragment. (Let me give you an example of a sound translation from English to French, Marcel Bénabou's transformation of "A thing of beauty is a joy for ever": *Ah, singe débotté, / Hisse un jouet fort et vert* — "Oh, unshod monkey, / Raise a stout green toy!")

In these two examples the sense of the original has been quite forsaken. Even when they preserve the sense, however, Oulipian renderings hardly resemble normal ones.

Third translation: "At this place and time exists the goddess of love identified with the Greek Aphrodite, without reservation taking firm hold of her creature hunted and caught." Explanation: each word has been replaced by its dictionary definition.

Last translation: "Look at Cupid's mamma just throttling that god's chump. Explanation: all words containing the letter *e* have been excluded."

The preserved sense hardly makes these two translations faithful ones. And yet all four examples can be considered translations. What has been translated, however, is not the text's nominal sense but other of its components; and we may call these components "forms", taking "form" simply to mean a material element of written language that can be isolated and manipulated. So the first pair of examples are direct translations of forms: in the passage from one language to another, forms rather than sense are what is preserved (number of letters, sound). The second pair are replacements of forms — not only the words but a form of the original has been replaced, in one instance a lexical context, in the other the choice of vowels.

These strange dislocations of the original may seem cavalier, but they are useful in drawing attention precisely to elements of language that normally pass us by, concerned as we naturally are with making sense of what we read. Nominal sense becomes implicitly no more than a part of overall meaning. Jacques Roubaud has recently provided a nice insight into its relativity in a discussion of the nature of poetry. He posits the axiom, "Poetry does not respect the principle of non-contradiction", and goes on to propose two poems for comparison (since Roubaud says they are poems, let's agree):

1st poem: This is a poem.

2nd poem: This is not a poem.

There is, he asserts, no poetic contradiction between the two poems. I would add that, according to ordinary criteria, the second poem is not a translation of the first; whereas by Oulipian criteria, they are perfect translations of one another — just as "*Je suis français, Monsieur!*" and "I'm American, and you better believe it!" can be considered equivalents even though saying different things.

This view of translation is a first clue to why the Oulipo has something to teach anyone interested in how writing and reading work.

The Truthful Liar

The American novelist Robert Coover writes fiction that can be mildly described as outlandish. It is full of banal situations rapidly transformed into comic nightmares. No one would call him a realist. Yet at a literary conference several years ago, when he was asked why he wrote, he answered, "To tell the truth."

His answer startled me; not that Robert Coover isn't an honest man, but this was not what his work first brought to mind. I quickly saw that he had been right to place himself in an age-old tradition of poetic truth-telling. In that case, we may then ask, why does he invent tales so unlike what we see around us? Why can't he simply say what is true?

He could simply say it; what he cannot do is simply write it. We can tell the truth when we speak; it may not happen often, but you know it when it happens. But when you write down what you say, whether it's "I love you" or "Pass the salt", the words in themselves are no longer either true or untrue. No one is there to be responsible for them.

Even in its ordinary, utilitarian uses, the written word cannot guarantee what it says. Can we agree that instruction manuals sometimes fail to help? Although once you've figured out your gadget, they become clear enough. Have the cooks among you tried out cookery book dishes that clearly had to be mastered before you could understand the recipe? The authors of manuals and cookery books tell us honestly what they do, but because they aren't there to show us, it doesn't work.

Consider the press. (If you watch your news, notice that the person on television speaks a written text.) What do we want from a news report? Hard information — what we call facts. And what are facts? What, for instance, is the central fact about a tennis match that you learn in a newspaper? The final score. Does that mean the score is the match? After three hours of play, Sampras and Agassi are tied two sets apiece and 4-all in the last set: where is the final score? Nowhere to be seen. The score only comes into existence when the match passes out of existence.

Facts are the score, not the game. Facts are lies. Not because they are false, but because facts belong to the past — to what was, never to what is. We love them, because once reality is safely lodged in the past, it becomes reassuring, reasonable, and easy to manage. Or at least easier: we read, "50 Palestinians and 12 Israelis killed in renewed fighting", barely gulp, and turn the page. Naturally. That is the way written language naturally works. Our language is made up of devices called sentences and paragraphs that automatically produce reasonable conclusions, which is another word for facts.

There is no escaping this. It is not a Bad Thing. However, a reality we can call the truth must be looked for elsewhere.

Fragment of a Neosocratic Dialogue

Scene: outside the wall of Athens.

You have been silent for a long time, Socrates.

I have been observing these little statues, Echecrates. This shady spot must be dedicated to Proteus.

I thought that you might be falling asleep. The breeze is so soft, the brook makes so lulling a sound, and then the air is filled with such a sweet scent of wild thyme.

It is abundant enough and makes a pleasant couch; but I am not sleepy, Echecrates.

All the same, you seem little inclined to speak.

Perhaps.

So you prefer silence, Socrates?

Let me listen to you, Echecrates. Will you agree to consider a question, one that you, better than anyone, can surely answer?

What is your question?

Echecrates, tell me: what is the truth?

Socrates, I expect you wish for silence after all, and that you hope to keep me quiet with your proposal. I shall not let you off so easily but answer your question forthwith. The truth is the perception of Ideas, which are the sole causes of all things and the sole objects of knowledge.

Your answer, Echecrates, is apt; for certainly the knowledge of truth requires the perception of Ideas. And yet the truth is not that.

In that case, Socrates, let me modify my answer, for I see that the truth lies of course not in perceiving but in what is perceived: the truth, then, is the divine array of absolute forms by which the One is manifest in the Many, and the Many subsumed in the One.

What you say is by no means false, since no opinion of the truth can deny its unity or exclude its multiplicity. And yet, Echecrates, the truth is not that.

If only I could guess what you expect of me! Socrates, you have turned me into a confused child standing before a stern and patient father, hoping to please and dreading to disappoint him. Let me try once more to satisfy you. The truth is what is apparent only to the dead, whose immortal souls are freed from the hindrance of the bodily senses and are at last capable of knowing the pure and the good.

Let us hope, Echecrates, that we two are carried to that realm of virtuous souls, where we shall converse with Orpheus and Homer and know ourselves at last. But I feel that my question wearies you, and that the time has come to put it aside. Only in conclusion, let me repeat what I said before: the truth is not that.

But is there an answer to your question, Socrates?

Yes, and I have given it to you.

Socrates, I do not understand.

I have given you the answer three times. The truth is: not that. Is not this so, Echecrates? When we define a thing, is the definition ever perfectly satisfying, that is to say, complete?

No, Socrates, never.

I agree, Echecrates. There is always something missing; there is always more to be said. So however you define it, whatever words you assign to it, you can and must always say afterwards, the truth is, not that.

Keep Moving

If Neosocrates is right, saying that the truth is "not that" implies: whatever you think you know, don't stop there. How can this apply to what has already been said?

Earlier I reached the conclusion, facts are lies. What if I round that out: facts are lies — and that's a fact. Look at what happens now. Facts are lies, and that's a fact: if the statement "facts are lies" is a fact, then the statement is a lie; and if it's a lie, then facts aren't lies. But in that case the fact that facts are lies is a lie, and so saying that facts are lies is not a lie, and so facts are in fact lies, and the statement "facts aren't lies" is a lie — and that's a fact. And so on and so on.

This modest circular paradox has its interest. First of all, when we read or hear it, something occurs beyond what's being said. Second, what was previously a conclusion becomes a continuum, a succession of events rather than a single event. What is the main difference between a conclusion and a continuum? What distinguishes the final score of a tennis match from the moment when Agassi and Sampras are tied 4-all in the fifth set? Uncertainty and movement; in a word, change, a quality that is wholly wanting in the realm of facts. Change can have no place among facts, which constitute the realm of fatality, of what's over and done with. The realm where change exists is that of possibility.

"Not that" suggests that truth is a continuum of uncertain possibility. It only exists in the next now. In writing, that means the now of reading. Since the first reader is the writer herself, a truth-telling writer has to create the possibility of not yet knowing what the truth is, of not yet knowing what he or she is going to say. Non-writing artists seem to grasp this easily. Francis Bacon described his painting as "accident engendering accident." Ornette Coleman said he never knew what he was going to play next until he heard the note coming out of his saxophone. One writer, at least, made the point neatly: when the Red Queen tells Alice to hurry up and say what she thinks, Alice replies, "How can I say what I think till I see what I say?"

If we think of writers as translators, what they must translate is not something already known but what is unknown and unpredictable. The writer is an Oho who has just heard what the Uhas say. Poor Botherby couldn't begin to cope: he wanted to report a fact when what he needed was a cultural revolution. Fortunately, we have the necessary means, not always revolutionary. Language creates a continuum of its own, precisely in those components that concern not the plain sense of words but what we noticed in the circular paradox, the movement that their sequence engenders.

Translation and the Oulipo (2)

If truth is a changing continuum and not a series of discrete events and ideas, it's unlikely that we can catch up with it in any reasonable way. Reasonable and honest accounts will always resemble superior instruction manuals, useful, even fascinating, never the thing itself. Or perhaps we should say a thing itself. On the page, truth begins when something real happens.

Imaginative writers officially disclaim reasonableness and honesty. That's what imaginative (or creative) signifies: they're lying. Poets and novelists are outright liars. They promise to provide no useful information unless they feel like it. Three advantages accrue immediately. First, you are released from all responsibility to the dead world of facts. Second, your readers are ready to believe you, since by admitting you lie, you've told the truth at least once. Third and best, you can discover the unforeseen truth by making it up. You are condemned to possibility: you can say anything you like.

So much freedom can be unnerving. If you can say anything, where do you start? You have already started. No one sits down to write in the abstract, but to write something. Some writerly object of desire has appeared, and you are setting off in pursuit of it. The object may be an anecdote, an idea, a vision, an effect, a climate, an emotion, a clever plot, a formal pattern — it doesn't matter, it is what you're after.

What happens next? The process of translation as it is commonly practised provides a helpful analogy. I am speaking from my own experience, but I do not think it exceptional.

Simplistically described, translation means converting a text in a source language into its replica in a target language. Both translators and readers know what happens when this process is incomplete: translators become so transfixed by the source text that when they shift to their native tongue they drag along not only what should be kept of the original but much more — foreign phrasing, word order, even words. The results hang uncomfortably somewhere between the two languages, and a brutal effort is needed to move them the rest of the way.

I learned how to avoid this pitfall. When I translate, I begin by studying the original text until I understand it thoroughly. Then, knowing that I can say anything I understand, no matter how awkwardly, I say what I have now understood and write down my words. I imagine myself talking to a friend across the table to make sure the words I use are ones I naturally speak. It makes no difference if what I write is shambling or coarse or much too long. What I need is not elegance but natural, late-twentieth-century American vernacular. Translating the opening sentence of Proust — *Longtemps je me suis couché de bonne heure* — I might write down: When I was a kid, it took me years to get my parents to let me even stay up till 9. (This is actually *mid*-twentieth-century vernacular; but that's where I'm from, and it's what I might say.)

There is still work to do. But I have gained an enormous advantage. Instead of being stuck in the source language, I am standing firmly on home ground. My material is as familiar as anything in language can be; and instead of having to move away from the foreign text, I can now move towards it as I improve my clumsy rendering, sure that at every step, with the source text as my goal, I shall be working in native English. All I have to do is edit my own writing until I eventually reach a finished version.

Think of the writer's object of desire — vision, situation, whatever — as his source text. Like the translator, he learns everything he can about it. He then abandons it while he chooses a home ground. Home ground for him will be a mode of writing. He probably knows already if he should write a poem, a novel, or a play. But if it is a novel, what kind of novel should it be — detective, picaresque, romantic, science fiction, or perhaps a war novel? And if a war novel, which war, seen from which side, on what scale (epic, intimate, both)? At some moment, never forgetting his object of desire, which may be the scene of a thunderstorm breaking on a six-year-old girl and boy, he will have assembled the congenial conventions and materials that will give him a multitude of things to do as he works towards realising that initial glimpse of a summer day, a storm, and two children.

An example can make this clearer. Throughout his life, Robert Louis Stevenson was fascinated by the dual personality. His greatest exploration of the theme was *The Master of Ballantrae*, but he tried other ways of approaching it. In one instance he chose as his home ground the 19th-century penny dreadful with its array of melodramatic and grotesque trappings. Stevenson saw that to discover the mystery of his object of desire — the dual personality — in its starkest terms, these trappings provided what he needed. They proved so suitable that we scarcely notice them when we read *Doctor Jekyll and Mr. Hyde,* a work successful enough to have attained the status of a modern legend.

It would be interesting to investigate works whose home grounds are not so readily discernible; it would also be laborious, and it is now time to think about the Oulipo.

Back home at the Oulipo

Since the mid 19th century, writers have chosen their home grounds more and more outside the main traditions of fiction and poetry. Firbank used the brittle comedy of manners to register his tragic views; Kafka turned to the parable; Hofmannsthal and Calvino on occasion to fairy tales; Henry Miller to pornography. Other writers invented their own home grounds — Mallarmé in poetry, for instance, Joyce and Raymond Roussel in fiction — and it is for their successors and their readers that the Oulipo has a particular relevance.

A parenthetical point: the Oulipo is not a literary school. It is not even concerned with the production of literary works. It is first and last a laboratory where, through experiment and erudition, possibilities of writing under arbitrary and severe restrictions are investigated. The use of these possibilities is the business of individual writers, Oulipian or not.

All the same, several members of the Oulipo have exploited Oulipian procedures in their work. I suggest that these procedures have provided them with home grounds. How is this possible? How can methods based on deprivation become the comforting terrain on which a writer sets out in pursuit of an object of desire? Why would anybody not a masochist want to determine a sequence of episodes according to the tortuous path of a knight across the entire chess-board? Or use the graphic formulations of a structural semiologist to plot a novel? Or limit one's vocabulary in a story to the threadbare words contained in a small group of proverbs? Or, if a poet, why use only the letters of the name of the person a poem addresses? Or, conversely, exclude those letters successively in the sequence of verses? or create a poetic corpus using the ape language of the Tarzan books? Nevertheless, these are some of the things Perec, Calvino, Jacques Jouet, and I chose to do, with acceptable results.

Why did we do them? I used to wonder myself. When I first learned that Perec had written a novel without using the letter *e*, I was horrified. It sounded less like coming home than committing oneself to a concentration camp.

When we were children, what we loved most was playing. After a fidgety family meal or excruciating hours in class, going out to play made life worth living. Sometimes we went out and played any old way; but the most fun I had was playing real games. I have no idea what games you enjoyed, but my own favourites were Capture the Flag and Prisoner's Base — hard games with tough rules. When I played them, I was aware of nothing else in the world, except that the sun was getting low on the horizon and my happiness would soon be over. In Manhattan last autumn, I stopped to watch a school soccer game in which an eight-year-old girl was playing fullback. She was alertness personified, never taking her eye off the ball, skipping from side to side in anticipation of the shot that might come her way. She had definitely not engaged in a trivial activity.

The Oulipo supplies writers with hard games to play. They are adult games in so far as children cannot play most of them; otherwise they bring us back to a familiar home ground of our childhood. Like Capture the Flag, the games have demanding rules that we must never (well, hardly ever) forget, and these rules are moreover active ones: satisfying them keeps us too busy to worry about being reasonable. Of course our object of desire, like the flag to be captured, remains present to us. Thanks to the impossible rules, we find ourselves doing and saying things we would never have imagined otherwise, things that often turn out to be exactly what we need to reach our goal.

Two examples. Georges Perec's novel without the letter *e*, intermittently dramatic, mysterious, and funny, describes a world filled at every turn with multiple disappearances. Some undefined and crucial element in it is both missing from it and threatening it — something as central as the letter *e* to the French language, as primordial as one's mother tongue. The tone is anything but solemn, and yet by accepting his curious rule and exploring its semantic consequences, Perec succeeded in creating a vivid replica of his own plight — the orphaned state that had previously left him paralysed as a writer.

I had a similar experience with my novel *Cigarettes*. My "object of desire" was telling the story of a passionate friendship between two middle-aged women. That was all I knew. I had concocted an elaborate formal scheme in which abstract situations were permutated according to a set pattern. This outline suggested nothing in particular, and for a time it remained utterly empty and bewildering. It then began filling up with situations and characters that seem to come from nowhere; most of them belonged to the world I had grown up in. I had never been able to face writing about it before, even though I'd wanted to make it my subject from the moment I turned to fiction. It now reinvented itself in an unexpected and fitting guise that I could never have discovered otherwise.

For Perec and me, writing under constraint proved to be not a limitation but a liberation. Our unreasonable home grounds were what had at last enabled us to come home.

The Case of the Persevering Maltese

Earlier I quoted Francis Bacon describing his painting as "accident engendering accident." Imposing fixed patterns as it does, the Oulipian approach sounds as though it discourages such self-generating activity, but this is not so: in practice it guarantees that the unforeseen will happen and keep happening. It keeps us out of control. Control usually means submitting reasonably to the truly tyrannical patterns that language imposes on us whether we like them or not. Language by its nature makes us focus on its conclusions, not its presence. Oulipian dislocations of this 'natural' language counter its *de facto* authority or, at the least, provide alternatives to it. Don't forget that language cares as little about our individual needs as the tides and the winds; ill-equipped, we can affect it no better than King Canute.

Those of you who have visited Venice may know the paintings of Vittore Carpaccio in the Scuola di San Giorgio degli Schiavoni. The *schiavoni* were Slavs, and the cycle of paintings concerns a patron saint of Dalmatia, St. Jerome. Surprisingly, St. Jerome is absent from the most beautiful of these pictures, "The Vision of St. Augustine"; but there is a good reason for this. St. Augustine sits at his desk, where he has just finished reading a letter from St. Jerome asking his advice on a theological matter. St. Augustine has scarcely taken up his quill to reply when light floods his study and a miraculous voice reveals to him that St. Jerome is dead.

It might be entertaining to speculate on the relevance of the scene to what I've been discussing — pointing out, perhaps, the futility of the reasoned answer St. Augustine is preparing in the face of the unforeseen and overwhelming truth. But let's not. We have a still more entertaining object to contemplate.

In the middle of the floor, to the left of the saint's desk, a little Maltese dog sits bolt upright. He is bathed with celestial light, to which he pays no attention as he stares at his master in an attitude of absolute expectation, as alert in his immobility as was my little fullback in her agile skipping. He is as unconcerned by the momentous event now occurring as he is by literary theory. His attitude might be translated as the human question, What next? Like children and Oulipians, he probably wants to play, but he can't be sure of that or anything else.

He has to wait to find out. What next? What next, and what after that? The answer will be something like the one given by Marcel Duchamp when asked what he considered the highest goal of a successful life. He replied, "*It*. Whatever has no name."

Lans-en-Vercors – Paris, 23 October 1996

ARMENIAN PAPERS

A Venetian Palimpsest

During a stay in Venice in the late winter of 1979, in the company of the French novelist Marie Chaix and the American critic David Kalstone, I paid a long-anticipated visit to the Armenian monastery of San Lazzaro, built on an island in the lagoon between the city and the Lido. On the recommendation of Signor Arsène Yarman, we were warmly received by the Father Superior, Padre Gomidas, who devoted well over two hours to guiding us through the monastery, known to Armenians the world over as a centre of their traditional culture, and to readers of English literature as the site of Byron's retreats from the excesses of Venetian society.

When Padre Gomidas led us into the famous library, already restored from the damages done by the fire of 1976, Professor Kalstone asked him if any manuscripts or incunabula had been lost in that conflagration. None, replied Father Gomidas, that were of the first importance; and in the ensuing discussion he mentioned, as the very type of a truly catastrophic loss, a manuscript of medieval poems that had mysteriously and irrevocably disappeared during the decade preceding the First World War, long before (he sighed) the invention of microfilm or reprography. When, intrigued by the undisguised intensity of his feelings in the matter, we questioned him further, he revealed that, because of indifference and incompetence, no copy had ever been made of the manuscript, whose text was nowhere else to be found. It was not that the poems that comprised the text were of great literary value, but that they were unique both in subject matter and in style. Their author had never been identified, although some nineteenth-century scholars had lamely ventured such names as Aristakes di

Lastivert and Grégoire Tlay; nor had the events related in the poetic sequence been convincingly linked to any known precedent in Armenian history, literature, or legend, a puzzle compounded by the incompleteness of the sequence, which virtually ended with the thirtieth of its forty-nine poems.

Father Gomidas had by this time succeeded in contaminating us, and especially the author of these lines, with his almost obsessive interest in the lost work. Had no description of the work survived it, we asked, no gloss, no excerpts in literary histories or anthologies? The Father Superior seemed surprised at our sudden curiosity, perhaps even faintly suspicious. We then confessed our calling; reassured that he was addressing professional writers, one of whom at least was a scholar, he went on to tell us that no such helpful clues to the nature of the work were known to him. One document alone remained: a translation made during the 1870s during a visit to the monastery by the young Arturo Graf, helped most probably by one or several of the Armenian inmates.

Arturo Graf (1848-1913) was a poet of considerable reputation, originally a disciple of Carducci, the influence of whose *versi barbari* (accentual adaptations of Greek and Latin quantitative verse) was still overwhelming at the time of his sojourn in the monastery of San Lazzaro. A less fortunate style for the rendering of medieval poetry can hardly be imagined, although poor Swinburne must once again be called on to supply a comparison that he does not, once again, altogether deserve. The Father Superior's indignation was in part founded on the, to him, radical inadequacy of Graf's work. The poet had apparently used the original poems as no more than a pretext for the pursuit of his own, quite contemporary concerns (a procedure not blameworthy in itself but, in view of the disappearance of the exploited manuscript, painfully regrettable). Father Gomidas illustrated his point with a line from poem XXXIX:

fresche a voi mormoran l'acque pe'l florido clivo scendenti
(to you fresh waters murmur as they run down the flowered cleft)

Although all of poem XXXIX is, even in Graf's translation, focused on depicting a landscape empty of human beings and parched by a desiccating wind, Graf introduces the anomalous phrases *a voi* (to you) and *florido clivo* (flowered cleft), the latter after making the point that even "weeds [are] as dry as harvested stalks" (my version). The explanation for this absurdity is not without interest: it turns out that the guilty line is a quotation from Carducci himself. Again, paying such a tribute to his master is not in itself to be criticised. It does, however, demonstrate Graf's indifference to any kind of fidelity to his original.

Father Gomidas consented to make me, on a modern machine lodged in the rooms of the prestigious, centuries-old press, a copy of Graf's translation. Since then I have spent many hours contemplating it, imagining the original poems from which it derives, imagining how those originals, if they existed, might have been Englished. The work that eventually issued from the time so passed is in truth less than paper-thin — a shadow cast by some phantasmal thing deduced from the evidence of other shadows; and the account I have here given of its genesis is not presented as a justification, merely as a way of saying that no justification for the work exists, that in itself it can be said to exist scarcely at all except as a desperate hypothesis. Even less substantial, of course, is the presence of the original author, although my true and even less credible ambition has been to divine his almost but not utterly lost identity — not his name, but his character, and his intentions in writing his poem. Why, above all, did he devote himself to this account of unknown events of an unknown time and place? Was it he who then chose to remain himself unknown? The pages that follow inscribe my guess, my guess of a guess, at answering these remote and ghostly questions.

Paris, February 22, 1985

I

When the virgin stepped out on the flagstones, she was not allowed to speak, not even words not of her choosing. It wasn't that pity might disturb the feast but that her speaking would distract from its object to herself. No matter how willing, she must remain instrument and victim. Staring over half-munched fritters, men were consoled for returning to the front (or to their scrolls) — what was time wasted set against this waste? Women felt heroic responsibilities in their sex, a junction of deprival and strength. And the children sang as they went, complying with instructions sternly rehearsed, justifying the confidence shown in them: their hymns grew stronger as they advanced along the highway towards their goal. The contentment on their faces differed from the contentment, if that is what it was, of the young woman. As I looked around me, I saw among others what I myself was feeling, a pride familiar (as in one's own family), and this has probably withstood the failure of the sacrifice, the desolation of the city, the years of massacre and captivity.

II

Old men tell us: we respected the seasons. Now November has followed November with confusion in between. Picking up scraps of glory in mud or snow (more to reassess than reassemble them), we endure these old men as bearers of beauty, bearing it away. They tell us how everything used to happen and was worse — that winter of dry wind; the snowy summer when half our peasantry emigrated; our own, internecine slaughters. We agree. Methods of supply are becoming more efficient, an improvement unquestionable by the living, of whom there are, also, more to be seen. Old men remind us that in hopelessness gifts flourish, indulgences fade. So then how soon shall I be cured of speech? The old men, the still-beautiful girls: by nature, averse.

III

Weeks of rain have nourished new green in blackened parks. In the gardens of the temple, where a flattening hand had swept, stubs of columns were righted on thick grass in a customary, elliptical alignment: today, first horse race. A race, maybe. But horses? These wizened hulks? The gamblers — optimists and bankers — are content; it will be cheerier than two dying dogs in a hole. A girl will be riding, Sirvan, Toram's daughter. I have decided to stay home and work on my book, my stories of another time and land. In another time, my mare was glossy as a mallard, her fetlocks were slim as wrists, and her clipped hooves struck the ground like fingers plucking strings. Sirvan won, and leads her horse by, with a vinous following. Her hair now loosed has a mare-like sheen. Tomorrow, horse soup.

IV

Baseboards underline my four walls: work of my inept hands, of my stubbornness in ineptitude, which has inspired cleanliness, assiduity at home and at the market, and an undermining awareness that beauty, like time, is not lost but abounds unjustly. I mean only that once again pots of wildflowers adorn my lair. Looking at them, I tremble (not really) with tenderness, yearning, jubilation. Anxiety, too: it was while I was unearthing a clump of red saxifrage that Dor accosted me. I felt no surprise, I was ready for his zeal, he gave me no difficulty. It was in my own mind that obligation rose from her unmourned grave and suddenly stretched forth her motherly bronze arms. There is this to do (impossible) and that (sure death), and we must, we must because otherwise. . . And I wouldn't give up a prune to the struggle for our identity, but in obligation thrives hope at its hopeless best.

V

Even abandoned orchards are bearing fruit. At break of dawn I pick what I can carry crossing the plain and by sun-up, far into the forest, reach my tended clearings. In hills nearby I have lighted the still each day — I'll have brandy for the year and a little for ageing, if no one finds me out and I improve my skills. Two months of paternal apprenticeship, stern as it was, left me a hacker. In former times I couldn't have sold a pint on credit. Now, for my raw booze, men and women, old and young (but there are few young women) force scallions and wool into my hands. I do my best, scouring my pots, curing oak for my kegs, discarding all first and last distillations, waiting out slow ferments of apple or plum. When I sit in the darkness of never-harvested firs, the fruit over smokeless charcoal seethes so faint you can hear a butterfly's flapping, or a wren as it hops up the crannies of a wall: the wall my father rebouldered, in the last summer of our life together, truncated by a Settler's axe.

VI

Written down, some feelings crave fixed patterns, with rhyme and metre, emphatic repetitions, or subtler symmetries; but I resist their delight, the delight of invocations and antiphonies, so as not to miss the point I'm making to myself — as if they directed the gaze from a woolly groin to the polite exposure of the columbine.

The truth in its immediacy is irregular. Even a moment later, regularity is still too late. Blood-spill from a punched nose, like adzed loppings or the sequence of emotions during birth, is belied when enlisted in the tropes of denser perceptions and justifications.

My mother died away from here, in the second autumn. They say she was not killed, something hard to believe, schooled as she was in sacrifice and endurance. There was nothing I could do: nothing I can now do except conceal that my grief is over. Another sort of grief, which her removal revived and which will not end, came long before then. I felt when she died that I had lost my child.

VII

Last night one Settler was stabbed between two doors. Another came to my stall this noon: the murderer, he said, had been drunk on my liquor. He looked into my eyes, revealing nothing. I turned hot, dizzy, and cold. Smiling — only a little, not to compromise me — he whispered, "May I sample the potion of valour?" and then publicly shouted, "A pint of your sow piss," stalking away with it. Not for some minutes did I notice the silver on the deal plank — my first coin of such worth. One face shows a sheaf of wheat, which stands for the goddess Khirkussia; the other is a profile of Vant. Is it a lie that Vant was their enemy and harried them out of one kingdom into ours? Have they no coin or king of their own?

VIII

Three days after the race, Sirvan was removed. Remoter farms were searched by night: we lost the few girls spared us. But "Rough seas cast up trophies", and it was then I came to sleep with Dor's mother, Ahaz's widow, entrusted to me. She was tender, fragrant, knowing, letting me in the breaks of desire at last mourn. I cried myself dry over and over, sucking patience from her grey eyes, marvelling at the autumnal brows and supple legs, gulping the potion of valour against sleep, one night, another night; and on the second bitter morning of dissolving fog Dor returning came to my threshold and took her home. I fetched fresh water and spent the day within my walls, writing in my book. I must spend all tomorrow in the hills, making up the brandy missed, and cutting firewood. Mine had been stolen from my yard — a small price; a warning, too, that this is not a time for passionate attachments.

IX

I was sniffing Içlan's swappable oil at my stall when he corked the jar and left. The Settler stood in front of me, "Potion of valour" himself. His stance suggested contempt, but his voice was pleasant: "In my domain are wine-growers who have delighted emperors. Our vines run across hillsides the length of valleys; orchards fill the lowland meadows. We have vats tall as two men where wine rests three years undrawn, and small old casks for brandy to yellow. In the lucerne-grass of the meadows, among the pear trees, are cattle to eat and milk; ewes on the hilltops; swine and geese in the yards, among towers of firewood. The kitchens blaze all day. Not even the harvest help is thin. Indoors, I have a library somewhat underused. Of your young women, eighteen are in attendance, only twelve with men of mine. You have a lot to learn, and know it, and know how. My name is Parno. I invite you to live with me."

X

I get up in the dark and walk two hours to the still; spend four hours lighting it, tending it, shutting it down; two hours back. A pocketful of dried fruit I eat standing as I barter my booze, swallowing with it pity for families my father loved, old women, old men, children, begging for easier terms. I think of my father: I will survive unulcerated. In late afternoon (dusk in this season) I haul my cart of earnings home to cook pork rind and leeks, to stare at the precious leaves of my slow-growing book. (Where are the white-handed teachers who came to embrace my parents at every vintage and called me their son?) I lie down in the dark to not sleep, and then sleep; and in the dark I get up and set out for my workplace. Parno spoke to me a week ago. Wedged in the wall boulders by the still this morning, a note from him: "I came here last month. Your kinsmen killed my two sons during the Settlement. No one will learn from me where you now stand reading. I know that you will survive; little more than that. I offer you more than that, and invite you to live with me."

XI

The attractions: solitude and secrecy — the orchard in the hills like a kingdom, the forbidden manufacture of liquor a prowess all my own, blessed with the contemplation of fir and beech, wild plum and cherry, and the company of the shy marten and jay as well as of cocky wrens and wagtails; the challenges of hiking, labour, and barter; the relief of exhaustion; the reassurance of a smartly contracted horizon; the refuge of my dwelling, small, neat, and warm, with its pots of flowering wall-paper and thyme, my pet dormouse staring around the thyme, and the new icon over my writing stool whose wood shines in the clear flame of stenchless fresh oil; soft if short hours in the lamplight, pen in hand, showered with the random amber of phantasmal summers, abundances, triumphs of art; visits from the widow.

XII

Others besides Parno heard of my brandy: yesterday two young Settlers were waiting at my stall. They slipped a noose over each shoulder, tied my hands, mounted high-strung horses, and tugged me between them to the next ex-town. I arrived hungry, not tired — five hours on a path was almost pleasant; time enough, anyway, to think away my fury. (Only in mortal danger would Parno be invoked.) I was led before a "Rector", an agile hooligan to whose redundant questions I did not deign to reply. Threats; a bloody nose; a night spread-eagled by four pegs under casually falling snow. Two hours before sunrise I was loosed, given dry clothes by a respectful Rector, loaned one lively horse for my return — a return perhaps infamous in the eyes of my fellows, such are the looks of reverence they cast me. Plainly some power has abided with me. One, nevertheless, not mighty enough to prevent my catching cold.

XIII

Dor came to me: the secret was out, I could no longer choose alone. He said it was my duty to leave, to be an ear and a voice behind their lines. Here I was an object of suspicion, I was no use to anyone (what of myself?), I disliked him: he was depriving me of arguments I had carefully saved; depriving me, too, because his visit forestalled another. Later, I was grateful — he authorised my yearning for Parno's flourishing lands. Dor said, "You are hardy, not unjust, only a little prone to dreaming that only your world is yours — that ours is not yours also. But you are ours: our soldier, our scribe." Opening my door, he turned into the darkness and turned back, saying, "Here is my mother. You have never saddened her. She will stay after me to make her goodbye."

XIV

The still was dismantled. Dumped ashes blotched the snow. The apple trees and plums will sprout wood next spring. The dormice will have the fruit to themselves. I bequeathed my dwelling to the companions of Dor, empty of everything but the mattress and withering pots. Piled under matting, my belongings rode on a rabbit-eared donkey (courtesy of the house) with whom I marched nine days, out of settled snows into a brown winter land, along a stream turning river, its banks mottled with grey then green, and after that a road climbing through hills of holm oak and brier through unkempt, severe greenness into a more useful display: a valley limy and dry, day marches of olive and vine, and beyond them thicker green on foothills and counterforts, from which granite ridges rose into a blaze of ice. This had been a time of smokeless inns, cold boiled tubers at cross-roads, nights in crammed corners of broken mills, snow-sodden boots, a depletion of anticipation and regret: then what was I to feel beholding this fatness if not the unreasonable conviction that my privilege was just and that it should not be my last?

XV

Today for the first time I shall enter the manor. The boils on my neck are drying up; the chronic fits of nausea and sadness are subsiding. During the last hot march, fever settled on me like an owl on a mouse, and I staggered into the farmyard like a drunk drunk — so I have been told, many times. Parno was away. My people were hoarding their luck. I was left to lesser Settlers — grooms, kennel guards, shit carriers, children. I sweated through days and nights, on last year's straw (my scrolls went under it when my cape was stolen, knitted by the widow from the wools of varied lambs). At last one beefy scullion found me comic. He nursed me with boiled fruit, wet cheese, sips of wine; until I thought, "Other survivals are worse," and moved out into sunshine. The others became used to my shabby strangeness. The chief wine-grower remembered I had been expected. He has promised to show me his vats. Now I have been summoned to the manor. Parno is back.

XVI

When he spied me from the far end of the hall, Parno turned away. Two or three figures next to him went out. He walked towards me with a fast, wary stride. I stopped, dropping my scrolls (I never budge without them). He took a long look at me, as though looking at a dead son. I longed to kill him. The scrolls unreeled: he asked, "What's that?" I told him about my book. I told him what had happened. He laughed. "No wonder you hate me." I began crying. "Now start over. Go to the baths, then the barber, then the tailor, then the cook and the wine steward! But barber and tailor first. Only an honest man could look the way you do — plague victim turned chimney sweep. Now come to your room, which is behind the library. Will you work in the library? (You can work with the wine people too, if you like.) Then you must begin mastering our script and syntax and idioms — your teacher has returned with me — tomorrow, if you're clean by then. This is what went wrong: the guardian assigned you lay sick in bed. One of your people here, having little love for them, or they for her. But of you she thinks well. Her name is Sirvan."

XVII

Sirvan had come to the hall to meet me, but Parno dismissed her because of my repulsive appearance. I did not see her for three days.

I was sitting at the foot of an orange tree when she rode by. I gaped insanely — it was like times before the Settlement. When I recovered, she had reached the neighbouring meadow.

Next afternoon she found me in the library. After bowing respectfully she giggled, apologetically — my head had been shaved (lice and gunk). She is fifteen.

My sensations had dwindled to disconsolate memories. I was grateful to her for new, real lust.

XVIII

Genna asserted, "There are seven powers, seven words — *pollian, suoph, ganarah, sutthi, hars, mlendan, hahir,* and they mean solitude, darkness, refusal, ignorance, impotence, poverty, and death." — I saw columns of black dust cruise through noon air, the wasted terrains, the evacuated ports, the treks of destructions sacrificing desire to endurance, the blood, the ashes, the mastery of fear. . . Watching me, Genna laughed and pointed through the window: ten big boys and girls were playing ball, each with more poise and lift than our dancers. (Some of my people watching, with officious respect — and thinking what?) "First learn our words and their use. The reasons will follow, or rather will not, but by then you won't miss them. You will know our powers for what they are: nothing more than a recognition of helplessness in the face of a destiny that does not exist."

XIX

"*Pollian*: with whom can the well-attended sympathise? or who with them? The idyll of the mother unfolding, enfolding, at next pain turns to immortal unforgivingness — fields of wheat set ablaze, familiar women peddled or ploughed under, unknown men scheduled into dreams of evisceration. . . So then: set the infant apart, in anxiety; set the child apart, in anger; set the adolescent apart, in longing; and the young women and men will behold that all has been theirs since the miracle of their birth, since their conception, since the conception of those who engendered them. They pass with ascetic joy through the gates of the city, stripping the useless past from their knowledgeable limbs, licking the rim of their glass in exuberant apprehension. Later, when the city is besieged, the wheat fields burnt, without hatred or regret they will swing open portals of new time, building unremittingly in their soul the visionary city from which no enemy is excluded. Once you know you are abandoned, compassion is yours."

XX

"*Suoph!* And darknesses, too, are replicated for us, childhood a gloom after gloom. We take our first steps at night. And it's you who are blind. You see the breast shining: happiness is that breast. You see the honey drip: pleasure is honey. You see the arrow pierce: food is an arrow. You see the lover's thrust: desire is a thigh. But those who learn to walk by night, who know daylight only through cracks of doors until their strength and wit can open those doors (some wait six years), what do they see when they step into the sun? They see light, not the things in it. They know that in themselves already happiness, pleasure, and desire are flourishing, not in the world, which is a sea to swim in, things merely tools in that soft blaze, O illuminated flesh! Thighs and arrows only tools to impress their desire on the tidal sumptuousness in which flesh is froth."

XXI

Ganarah: "Have a fig, please. Do you like figs?" I accept; the dusk-blue, donkey-nozzle pouch splits in my fingers; I hold it to my lips; Genna slaps it out the window — "Think: what is fig?" — then gives me another, as ripe. I eat it. "Think: fig, nature of fig." And: "Which time did you learn about fig?" Picking seeds from teeth, sucking teeth for last wine cellar sweetness, I perceive that I have lost fig in a procedure of figginess: "So, the first. But if I'd never tasted one?" Genna sighed: "Tell me about your first fig." "Before I remember." "Before you were born. Get out of here — Parno's expecting you."

I ran down to the chamber turned shrine (Sirvan there, too, honour to both of us): the mother of his son, and the baby son. Salt on skin; candles on sill.

XXII

That evening: in the gloom of a passageway, a forearm against my throat, a lump of wet flour jammed into my mouth; sack over head; rope around wrists and knees. On some giant shoulder, I was trundled through rooms into a place that smelled of beeswax and rose. I was gently lowered, stripped gentlier still (the giant's feet having exited). When the sack was rolled off my face, the young body squatting on mine was Sirvan's. "Why didn't you come? Why don't you come?" or some such joke — she was smooth, untechnical, not to be resisted, although I huffed at the flour lump and threshed against my bonds. She was watching me carefully. When I gave in she squealed like a queen of the castle and bent down on me like a flock grazing a pond.

Genna laughed: "You're a lucky numbskull! What we think, what we think we know, fights what is happening to the death — sometimes our own." He said this would serve as my lesson in *sutthi*.

XXIII

Imposing your desire, you acted like a man.

    "You like a woman, hiding yours."

I was treated like a woman. Now the giant will tell.

    "To secure his help, I swallowed shame."

They know we lay together. You have harnessed me to love.

    "I knew you were in love from last week's yard gossip."

How can you respect me after such disrespect?

    "My respect shows in my service. Your word is my rule."

For my submitting, my mother would die again.

    "I kneel to her ghost and beg her to bless me."

In me, my mother still lives out her life.

    "For one moment you forgot her, and now are mine."

If I am yours now, who do I argue?

    "Years of mourning, solitude, mistrust."

Not always solitude —

        "I knew Dor's mother.

She spoke of you. It is because of her that I am yours."

I'm foolish. Why didn't I court you? It's too late now.

    "Only for appearances. The story is on time."

XXIV

Hars: They took me away from her. Genna, with the giant in reserve, put me in a cell, the door bolted outside, the broad window out of reach. "You are through with women. Books and wine are your work and consolation." I was given little more: a mattress, a basin, a bucket, and each day with my bread another book, another jug of black wine; I threw down the books and threw up the wine. "Sirvan," I moaned, awake or dreaming. On the sixth day, the giant sat on me and bolted a strap around the cords of my testicles. A second week: pain gave way to a chafed swagger. I stopped eating altogether. A new moon came to the window. I wrote a poem on the chalky wall, needing bread after line two. It spoke of sap and snow. When I asked for my scrolls, the giant unstrapped me. A tray of broth and fish lay in the door left open on the hall where she sat, cross-legged in blissful light, Anaïd astride her new-woven universe.

XXV

To Sirvan by the brook appeared Dor dressed as a woman, sending me a message: meeting after last light where two stone fences cross on northern hill. I had one thing to tell him: if they see him, the three of us are dead. He sprang on me like a lover, in men's clothes: "*I'll talk.*" There are allies from the northeast, ruthless in combat, twenty villages freed already by their power and our stealth, and our own village soon. Will I return for the feast of vengeance and reclamation, or wait here? "How many men in this valley?"

I told him, "Men in this valley are dear to me. Our village is lost to those of our time. It's too late for vengeance. Have our allies left us the provinces they freed, are they returning to the northeast, or will their ruthlessness abide with us? Dor, are you happy at war? Do you love a woman? Stay here with me. Forget the dead and the death-giving." The stonebound olive groves rose towards the cusp of the hill. I knelt in front of him on the stones beneath which all the soft wealth spread under the moon. He said, "You understand my intention. Forget peace — it's for that it's too late. Tell Sirvan, so beautiful by the brook, tell your woman that."

XXVI

On another terrace, Parno was walking, his son in his arms. It was cool still; the dry air smelled of remembered mint. I told him that my life was in his hands; he replied that it had long been so. I said that I loved him more than my kind; he accepted my love. I spoke of Dor's visit; he asked, was *I* surprised? I begged for counsel, he tickled his son. "This is what you can do. First: move the older scrolls from the cabinets by the north wall (away from damp and mice) and copy them in order of decay. Next: a man from the southern mountains, an expert in distillation, is arriving tomorrow. Learn what he knows for use this autumn, and when he leaves, pick men to build your vats and stills. Then complete your lessons with Genna, who is a famous tactician and will soon reconnoitre the insurgent regions. Last, attend to your new dwelling, attend to Sirvan whom I destined for you, whom her candour, thin nose, and plaited hair make one of us. She will teach you how to think of past and future, barbarian dreams you should by now be outgrowing."

XXVII

Her feet smelled of tansy, her breath of apples. I sometimes was drunk: she begged me not to explain. When I shuddered at Dor's vengeance, she held a spike to my eye. When I was late elsewhere, she allowed me an hour's company. She was in the hills with the olive pickers, in the shed with the weavers, by the brook to beat cloth, home whenever I came. When she sang, blackbirds answered, and when she spoke, doves. She wore loose gowns that enabled me to imagine her. When I was vexed by my clumsiness, she spilled soup in her lap. Licking her neck, I thought *aloes*, not knowing what it was. When I said I was bored, she fell asleep as I said it. I could never hate or pity her; she insisted that these sentiments be acknowledged. She stroked me as though I were dough she would later bake. She was awake before I stopped dreaming, asleep after I began.

XXVIII

Our people's allies have simple, expedient gods; and no God, only a name to point back to; and they do not point back. They have adopted the scripts of five realms, ones they held and abandoned. (Before, they did not write.) They have no reputation as traders because they do not trade. Others trade for them, following precepts and expectations that are plain enough but rashly (so we hear) ignored. They never demand what is rare, any more than they respect it. As fighters, they are brilliant, because they look at time and space backwards: achievement is not behind them, it waits in the next valley, tomorrow at dawn. In this view, supply is the responsibility of the defenders, who with only their own past to defend yield to the newcomers in time, in little time, time past and forgotten to the victors as their losses are forgotten. As ours are not: Dor cut down with a billhook, far from his hearth, far from us.

XXIX

Mlendan: Only when written down do patterns become fixed, the leaf no longer growing, the petal stiff in the rain. Perhaps I should suggest leaves folded in darkness, I should lay down a suggestion of their hidden irregularities in words that cover themselves, one after another (words best of double meaning, so that uncertainty as to their function will blur forever the knowing eye).

Think of each season folded into itself and around its neighbour, and each year so folded, and hour. You shake out the first fold, perhaps a harvest moon, underneath is market time — a young man peddling brandy. You unravel this in turn, and next comes a fold — sad winter— that we pretend is the last; but the last, whenever it comes, will be a fold not-fold, a palpitation between future and past, a coming and going.

Our fellows, both men and women, said Sirvan had betrayed them: they took her away. (They know theirs was the betrayal, but they have had little practice in truth.) What is hard for me to tell is whether what was done enfolds what is to come, or what is to come, what was. The news travelled late to our camp. When I look at it, my breast portrait of Sirvan wavers: is my emptiness now what filled me up before?

XXX

Parno followed Genna north into the barren valleys, the ones down which I had journeyed from my village (now ours once again, though hardly mine). Our invaders had pushed farther south, raising up rebellion by their reputation as slaughterers, moving fluidly into the breaches of nature and their antagonists, attentive to night paths and fords briefly unwatched. The land that could be ceded to them, land empty or newly settled, would soon be theirs, they would perch on the hills above our plains; and two armies would so kill and be killed that winning would resemble extinction more than triumph. Parno went forth to rally men armed and unarmed. With Genna he incited the enemy to plunge into indefensible predicaments. With others he made the settlers into spies and messengers, men, women, children, weaving a slow-closing net of loyalty and shrewdness, entangling those forward-minded strangers by their own speed, making them at last look back. . . He was caught in a dead-end gorge into which his enemies had been driven, trapped by the trapped. At the end, he laughed and swore that no man could lessen the rapture of a living act, even if his last, even death.

["*Desunt epigrammata octo*"]

XXXIX

Habir. Showerings of bitter, ripe black olives from branches steadied in silveriness; the shadows of low stones clear as ciphers on the opposite side of the valley; a grey and orange cliff face enamelled as if fired; weeds as dry as harvested stalks in the abandoned fields; wailing of air unheard on hilltops and in the canyons; distant streaking smoke perhaps no sign of the living; plumes of dust rising in low twists from the ways; from horizon to peak of sky an insistent, withdrawn blue; and below and above a fierce cold burning, drying dry earth with scurrying thoroughness, imagined travellers shielding blistered faces even stooping to the dark glitter of streams — tiny streams trickling indifferent and undiverted, not a wisp of spray above their shallow vagrant grooves, their rock borders whistling day and night in the patient clarity: the yearning for relief will at last be answered, after a time whose duration does not matter, with billows of damp hurrying high through the air from a sea too inaccessible for naming or pilgrimage.

[*"Desunt epigrammata novem"*]

XLIX

SAINT GREGORY'S HYMN TO SAINT MICHAEL

Angel of light,
 at this doom's parting
 gather our smart
 against new soul's night.

Angel of death,
 for our new life
 bring sharp salt for shriving
 and a bitter wreath.

Angel who left us
 blinded with changing,
 our tongues estranged,
 our strained ears deaf:

You who shake out
 the folded seasons,
 give us surcease
 for our dead Lord's sake.

AUTOBIOGRAPHY

Here is an outline of my life:

I was born in New York on the Upper East Side at 2:40 a.m. on February 14, 1930. I was educated in private schools, first in the city, then at Groton School in eastern Massachusetts. I entered Princeton College in the fall of 1947. At the end of my third term I enlisted in the Navy for a year, in the course of which I married French-born, New York-raised Niki de Saint Phalle. I completed my college studies at Harvard, graduating with a B.A. in music in June 1952. A daughter, Laura, was born during our stay in Cambridge. I and my family moved to France in July 1952, and lived there — in Paris, Menton, and Nice — for over two years. (I studied piano and conducting for a few months before deciding to make a career of writing.) In the fall of 1954 we moved to Deyá, Mallorca, for two years; a son, Philip, was born in 1955. We returned to France in the summer of 1956, living first in Paris, then in Lans-en-Vercors in the French pre-Alps. Separated from my wife at the end of 1960, I came back to Paris with my children soon afterwards. My daughter left school and home in 1969, after which I settled in Lans with my son, who in turn ran away to America in 1972. I again lived in Paris until mid-1974, then in Venice for two years. While there, I met the French writer Marie Chaix, and I came back to France to live with her and her two daughters, from 1976 to 1986 in Lans, for the past year in Paris. During this period I began spending almost half of each year in America, where in 1978 I began teaching, first at Bennington College, later at Columbia. Since 1962 I have published four novels and six collections of poetry.

Family

I was born in Manhattan, on Saint Valentine's Day, 1930, of parents who had married on May 29 the year before. The interval of 261 days — just over thirty-seven weeks or eight and a half months — later made me suspect that my conception had precipitated my parents' marriage. (I believe that I once asked my mother if this were so and she calmly replied that it wasn't and explained why. I have meticulously erased from my memory the details of this conversation, if it ever took place.) It has always struck me as odd that my parents, both of whom were respectful of customs and devoted to *their* parents, chose to be married after the briefest of engagements in a summary, private ceremony. Nor did they ever consider having another child; indeed my mother, while extraordinarily fond of me, often expressed a dislike of children in general and wondered why anyone would voluntarily choose to have them. (Family planning was her favourite charity.) Events following my own marriage confirmed my suspicion that I came into the world by no means unloved, but probably unwished for.

Both my parents had been born into, and had remained dues-paying members of, the world of Upper East Side WASP respectability. Although neither was entirely happy in this world — my father had to curb a "difficult" character that might have felt easier in less polite surroundings; my mother longed for the styles and pleasures of Mediterranean Europe — neither questioned their adherence to it. In both their cases the source of this social loyalty is, I believe, to be found in filial devotion. My father adored and passionately admired his mother; my mother felt no less love for her father.

Edward Mathews's family on his father's side came from Philadelphia and Valley Forge, although he himself was born and raised in New York. My paternal grandfather, who died when my father was nine, was rarely spoken of by his children. His name evoked ghosts of irresponsibility. He had squandered his money and his privileges with the result that, when he died, his family was left in poverty — the genteel poverty of boarding-houses, admittedly, but a painful come-down all the same for people used to an easier life. My grandmother evidently reacted to these straitened circumstances wisely and courageously, making sure that my father and his sister got the best possible upbringing as well as the best education her disciplined thrift could provide.

Currie Duke, my father's mother, came from a respected Louisville family. She was the daughter of Basil Duke, second in command of Morgan's Raiders, descended from the Marshalls of Virginia. She was an exceptionally gifted violinist who studied with Joachim and made her debut at seventeen with the New York Philharmonic. After her husband's death, her musical skills enabled her to provide for herself and her family; but arthritis brought her musical career to a premature end. I first knew her as a kind, firm lady in her sixties, fearfully curbed in her activities by double cataracts, at that time a crippling affliction.

I was always astonished by my father's reverence and affection for this "poor old lady", as I childishly thought of her. For him she embodied the perfect mixture of gentleness and adamantine character. I think he would have endured any kind of pain to avoid seeing her in pain, or even offended. He paid a price for this, I'm afraid. He had once disappointed her by not going to college; he did his utmost never to disappoint her again. He had refused college because he was so eager to become an architect that he did not want to wait three or four years before starting work, and so he went straight into Yale Architectural School, paying his way by teaching drawing (he was an immensely gifted draftsman) at the art school of the university. The price I think my father paid for his filial respect was that of accepting architecture as a profession rather than pursuing it as an art. He had a successful career (when he retired he was a partner in Skidmore, Owings, and Merrill); he did excellent work for public and private clients; but he never relinquished the conventional ambitions of his profession to explore idiosyncratic, pioneer realms in the manner of Wright or Le Corbusier. To do that, he would have had to turn his back on the world of his upbringing, that is, on his mother's world.

I must admit to a bias in this matter. At the age of twenty I broke with my parents, deeply offending them, causing myself considerable suffering, spending years in an uneasy, ambiguous, indeed dishonest relationship with them. I am no longer so sure that I had to do this in order to write my novels and poems; but for years I was convinced that I would never have been able to write at all if I had not made this violent break. It is clearly tempting for me to tell myself that, no matter how modest my achievements, I did my father one better by pursuing the course I did.

My mother was the only child of Henry Burchell, son of an Anglo-Irish immigrant who made a fortune in cold-water flats, and Candida Paleari, a native of Monza in Lombardy.

My grandmother's background has remained a mystery to me. I presume that my mother once knew more about it than she was able to tell me. Judging from photographs of them together, I feel certain that my mother and grandmother were devoted to one another during my mother's early years. By the time I was born, that devotion had withered. As I grew up, my grandmother became increasingly deaf, solitary, cantankerous; my mother's daughterly love was increasingly directed to her father.

My grandfather and my mother had adored one another from the start. In his eyes she could do no wrong; and if she recognised his shortcomings, she was always more than ready to acknowledge his seemingly fathomless store of good nature and good will.

His chief shortcoming was his peculiar weakness. Intelligent, urbane, an amateur of all the arts, endowed with a fine gift for languages (he was a master of classical Greek and Latin, and he could speak and write Italian, French and German), competent in business matters, he suffered domestically and professionally from chronic timidity. He was frightened of his wife, who could scold him for spending fifty dollars on a new overcoat. He did not dare disturb strangers on whom his comfort might depend (I can still see him docilely waiting in line when his admission was already paid for); worst of all, at a crucial moment in his life he declined to defy his family when, after several gloriously happy years teaching Greek and Latin at Columbia, he was asked to give up his career. As the only brother not actively engaged in business, he was the obvious choice to "look after the family fortunes" — the reinvested wealth of the cold-water flats. My grandfather dutifully brought his life as scholar and teacher to an end.

For well-to-do men of my grandfather's generation, not working was not a disgrace; but my mother could hardly accept such a life as exemplary, especially after her marriage, when she had committed herself wholeheartedly to my father's career (not an easy one in the Depression years). She certainly deplored my grandfather's weakness towards her mother, who she felt cruelly deprived him of many pleasures in his later years, and she regretted his timidity towards the world at large, even if she could chuckle over its consequences. But I do not believe she would have wanted him different from what he was. She had an unqualified respect for the values he incarnated. He was quintessentially American in his honesty, forthrightness, and generosity; at the same time his knowledge and love of European culture — manners and attitudes as well as the arts, but most importantly the arts, of which the greatest was literature — distinguished him from the majority of his compatriots. He was the perfect gentleman; one furthermore whose loving attention had followed her from the day of her birth, something that may have left her a little spoiled but that understandably secured her lifelong devotion and loyalty.

Now my grandfather knew Europe well, and he had helped my mother know and love it in turn. He was, however, definitively settled in New York and entertained no serious thoughts of ever leaving the city. My mother, in spite of the strong attractions Europe had for her, one of them being perhaps the most intense love story of her life, followed her father's example and settled in the city where they had both been born. She did not attribute the responsibility of her choice to him; and I do not mean to suggest that without him she would necessarily or even probably have chosen otherwise. But her father's choice encouraged her own. It allowed her to live happily enough in America and at the same time to keep intensely alive the idea of Europe as a haven of pleasure, romance, and elegance — a view she staunchly maintained and sometimes vehemently expressed throughout her life.

If I have spoken at length about my grandfather, it is because of the influence he exercised not only on my mother but on me. During my first eighteen years he was a constant and considerable presence in my life, one I took great delight in. He was just over sixty when I was born, young for his years. From the first he unstintingly expended on me that attentive sweetness for which so many loved him. In my early childhood he often drove me to Central Park or to distant playgrounds he thought I might enjoy, patiently waiting for me to accumulate my afternoon's ration of bloodied elbows and knees. As soon as I could follow stories, he introduced me to the best of them he knew, reading aloud to me in the early evening from Grimm and Perrault and, a little later, book-length versions for children of the *Iliad* and the *Odyssey*. My interest in classical mythology having thus been awakened, he brought me other books drawn from it (and perhaps from classical history as well) for me to read myself. By the time I had reached fourth grade, ancient Greece and Rome formed a natural part of my imaginary world: so that it would have been inconceivable for me not to begin the study of Latin. My grandfather of course encouraged me in this, countering the dismays of the countless grammar lessons of the first years with promises of future delights — Catullus, Ovid, Horace. Later, when I growled with impatience at Cicero's orations, he would tell me, Wait till you read the letters; or when I struggled with the first book of the *Aeneid*, Wait till the fourth. And his encouragements extended far beyond the study of Latin, to reading in general (he lent me many volumes of Mark Twain after I discovered *Tom Sawyer*) and to listening to classical music. I believe it was my grandfather who gave me, at the age of nine or ten, the two 78-rpm records of leitmotifs in the *Ring of the Nibelungen* that opened up to me the world of Wagnerian opera, my first great aesthetic passion.

Or perhaps my mother gave me the records. Where matters of high culture were concerned, she and my grandfather acted as members of a team, with a clear, consistent purpose: I was to be exposed as often and as thoroughly as possible to the best composers, the best painters, the best writers of the West, in the last category especially to Shakespeare. Their purpose was not fuelled by class or cultural snobbery but by the intense, at times almost ecstatic pleasure they themselves found in high art (and in much low art, too). Because they were motivated by this spontaneous experience of pleasure, which was essentially the pleasure of knowledge in its sensuous forms, their efforts to share their experience with me attained their goal (even if, in the case of painting, that goal was attained only many years later, when I made my first trip alone to Europe; and even then their influence was manifest, since over the years they had nourished in me a longing to visit Europe, and especially Italy, where they had so often and so happily travelled together).

Of course the sensuous pleasure my mother took in art made art attractive to me for less obvious or at least less avowable reasons. She was a passionate, sensual woman, devoted to her only son. His upbringing, not to mention *her* upbringing (that is, her feelings about her father), prohibited expressing her sensuality and her passion to me overtly. Art and literature provided a vehicle for their less direct expression, and I quickly showed myself willing to play her game, one that no doubt I am still playing.

My mother claimed to dislike children, which meant the children of others, particularly girls. I was her own, and male. A place was cut out for me as the third of an exceptional series that had begun with my grandfather and continued with my father, a series of men committed to her happiness. Her designation of me for this role was not less evident for being unconscious; by which I mean that she lavished on me as a child and as an adolescent the same consideration, support, and patience (and her capacity for impatience was as large as her generosity) that she showed her father and husband. She was stern — reliably stern — in teaching me the techniques of politeness and cleanliness, as well as the necessary ethical hypocrisies of the class to which she belonged (ultimately no more hypocritical or less necessary than those of any class); she properly backed my father in his usually futile efforts to direct my energies to the world around me; but she never failed to forgive my shortcomings, to sympathise with my sufferings, or to share my sometimes wildly confused enthusiasms.

Here are some examples, trivial but relevant. When I had soiled my bed in my sleep around the age of five (an age well beyond any approvable limit), she dogmatically excused the accident as due to my having eaten unpeeled baked potatoes. She treated the horrendous juvenile acne with which I was afflicted between the ages of thirteen and eighteen with an awareness and reassurance that were more gratifying than any saintly commiseration. She read every author and listened to every composer that I discovered and by making my delight in my discovery her own gave me a recognition that in my ornery solitariness I was hard put to find elsewhere. Her loyalty to me gave me the possibility of accomplishing one of the most deceptive, destructive schemes of my life; that of becoming an element of discord between her and my father, of winning her as an ally in my utterly unnecessary combat with him.

As I have said, my father was a man of great talent, both as an architect and as a graphic artist. He was also a prodigious reader. He may have preferred Melville,

Prescott, and Kipling to my mother's favourite James, Wharton and Proust, but his sensitivity in literary matters was hardly inferior to hers. His sensitivity, indeed, was his weakness, and most of all in his own eyes. He looked for success in the approval of the well-to-do and preferably well-born businessmen and professional men among whom he had to make his career. There, his abilities as a fisherman and shot, combined with his charm and even his irascibility, could only serve him well. How could sensitivity, aesthetic scrupulousness, and doubt seem anything but unnecessary and useless to him, especially when he saw them magnified in his only son? He wanted me to be happy in the world — to be a good fisherman, to be manually and practically competent, to be sociable, to be successful. I caught the line of my rod in the nearest tree; I could not drive a nail home before I was eighteen; the notion of worldly success made me feel like a weasel on a rock pursued by a lunchless hawk. He loved me no less than my mother, but he wanted, or at least felt obliged, to make me into someone I had no chance of being. He sent me to summer camps when I longed to stay home. He took me fishing when I wanted to read, gave me kits for making model boats that paralysed me with bored incompetence (he finally made the boats himself), oversympathised with my love of baseball which on the playing field could not make up for my dismaying clumsiness. I didn't have the sense to discern the love in all this. I preferred to make him my enemy.

I engineered our opposition one evening when I was nine, perhaps a little older. I stole a set of disposable cigarette-holders from my mother's bureau drawers and hid them in my room. The place I chose to hide them was so conspicuous that I could count on their being found. My mother noticed their disappearance and promptly found them. When she asked me about them, I responded with patent lies. Not unreasonably offended, she told my father what had happened. The facts being as plain as my future pimples, he eventually forced me to admit them, whereupon he scolded me with exceptional sternness, at exceptional length, concluding with a homily on the virtues of honesty that hurt and humiliated me. For the first time in our relationship a moral absolute had been invoked, to my entire disadvantage. Since the insignificance of my fault clearly did not deserve such an anathema, I "learned" that my father totally disapproved of me and probably hated me. I told myself that I must never trust him again.

A few months later, a replay of the event — the conspicuous theft of five dollars, this time perpetrated while my father was away — enabled me again to provoke my mother and this time to secure through pitiful imploration the assurance of her silence in the matter. Through her silence she became my accomplice. Thereafter she remained my thoroughly bribed court of appeal in family disputes. My father was relegated to the inimical "outside world". It took me more than thirty years to realise that the enmity of that world was almost entirely my own creation, and that not only did my father love me but that I myself bore him so grateful and gratifying a love that when, at last, I allowed it to emerge into the light of consciousness, all my efforts to deny and pervert it had proved incapable of lessening its power.

In the meantime we waged our war. It had some happy truces: trips to the Florida Keys and the Bahamas on school vacations (after his return from the Pacific and the war), where I at last learned the joys of fishing; much later, working on the Long Island property he created, where he revealed unsuspected genius as gardener and landscape designer; and, later still, numerous summer evenings spent walking and talking together. These moments were few and brief. Our estrangement had been reinforced when I was nineteen years old by a more radical alienation that I had instigated: my marriage, which brought to an end my privileged relationship with my mother. From that time on, *both* my parents were excluded from what was central to my life. So at least I thought; so at least I wished.

In June 1949, a few months into my mid-college enlistment in the Navy, I eloped with Niki de Saint Phalle, the daughter of a French banker and businessman who had emigrated to the United States when she was two. I shall go into the whys of this event later on; whatever our reasons, they bore no weight with my parents, any more than did the ulterior series of justifications Niki and I spent much time inventing. Niki's parents, who had four other children, were offended but not bitterly so. My mother, however, faced with the abrupt removal of the son on whom she had lavished so much time and passion, behaved as though *her* daughter had been kidnapped and seduced. My parents tried energetically to undo what had been done — a waste of their time, since both Niki and I were of age. (My father's distinguished record as a Naval Reserve officer gave him enough influence to keep me stuck in the Norfolk Receiving Station through one steamy Virginian summer.) Eventually they resigned themselves to the inevitable, and Niki and I were publicly (re)married after my discharge from the Navy the following winter.

My relations with my parents, however, were to get worse. I had decided to finish college because I did not have the courage to disappoint my father on this score, and also probably because I was not sure what else to do. While I was at Harvard, the possibility arose of Niki's having a child. My mother, convinced that our marriage would fall apart, and the sooner the better, had a durable fit at this prospect. The violence of her opposition to Niki's pregnancy ensured its happening, and it also incited me (whether rightly or merely self-righteously some dispassionate witness alone can say) into breaking with my mother completely — that is, into refusing to see her or speak to her for a period of several months.

On April 23, 1951, our daughter, Laura, was born. From then on there was no question in my mind what the word "family" signified to me: it meant the one I had helped make, not the one into which I had been born. The latter now became part of the past, part of a difficult, hostile world, part of everything that I was eager to leave behind. Niki, Laura, and I embarked for Europe in the early summer of 1952, a month after my graduation. It could hardly be said that we were leaving America. Neither of us knew what America, or even New York, really was.

My parents proved patient. They were conscientious in trying to keep up their role as helpful family guardians. I'm afraid I was incapable of giving them any credit for that, interpreting their most helpful actions (such as providing Niki with the best available medical care in New York, when her thyroid trouble was at its dangerous worst) as attempts to meddle in our lives. The only reconciliatory gestures I approved of were those I could claim as my own. In 1959, for instance, when my beloved grandfather died, I insisted, over my mother's objections, on flying to New York to be with her, and, once there, I efficiently took charge of the disagreeable details of cremation and burial.

It was almost ten years later that, in order to restore the long-shattered relationship with my mother, I concocted a stratagem of unwitting brilliance, one that still delights me, all the more so for my obliviousness of what I was doing. I had bought two tickets for the *Ring* cycle at Bayreuth. Since I knew that my mother had a busy schedule that summer, I told myself that it would do no harm, and certainly entail no risk of her accepting, if I offered her my second ticket for the four performances. When a telegram arrived shortly afterwards announcing her arrival in Frankfurt on the eve of *Das Rheingold*, I was, nevertheless, anything but amazed. I would have been amazed, I realised, if she had declined to join me; I saw that I had never intended her not to be at my side when I visited the shrine of my "first passion".

And so, without a word of reference to our violent disagreements or our years of estrangement, we effected a reconciliation that was to prove lasting. We spent a happy week together, not only attending the operas that were its pretext but jubilantly fleeing the pompous horror of the Bayreuth opera crowd to investigate the various attractions of Lower Bavaria, of which Bamberg and the church of Vierzehnheiligen would alone have made the trip worthwhile — on this we agreed, and the agreement perhaps gave her the satisfaction of finding me properly aligned with the two other men in her life, with her two other favourite travelling companions.

Several years later, after participating in the course of a seminar I was taking in a demanding exercise called the "Truth Process", I discovered, tearfully and happily, that for much of my life I had been painstakingly transforming my parents into monsters, and that I had furthermore done this for no better reason than my own convenience. The ploy of the stolen cigarette-holders, the eagerness with which I'd seized the chance to belabour my mother with her wrongs during Niki's first pregnancy, and all the self-justifications consequent to those events were revealed to me as ruses to blame others for my displeasure at being in the world. This revelation brought me great relief. It also brought an annoying problem: how could I possibly tell my mother and father what I had just learned? The problem turned out to be imaginary. Paying them a visit the next day, I found, on entering the room where they were waiting for me, two people I had never seen before: in place of the redoubtable pair I was familiar with, an elderly man and woman overjoyed to see me, full as they were of a love that I suppose had never once failed them since my birth. I had nothing to tell them. I had nothing to do except look and listen.

I have written at length about my parents because I know that next to them most of the people who have figured in my life can only assume the roles of substitutes, replicas, replacements of this original man and woman. Most of the time, other people can only set an "objective" and partial reality against the imagined and absolute reality with which, out of the limbo of my first years, I invested the actual couple who engendered me. I have learned more from my own children (and from the children of my present companion) than I did from my father and mother; and I can say as much of the men and women to whom I have been closest. But these few, dearest others can never replace, only enlarge, the primordial family in which I discovered life in our world.

From the age of nineteen I did my best to deny the importance of this family, to pretend that whatever mattered in my life was of my own choosing and making. I tried to evince the notion of family from my dealings with the world and from my thinking about my life. I was painfully taught how deluded I was. Between the ages of thirty and forty-three, I "endured" the departure of my wife, my daughter, and my son (Philip, born in 1955). During my years of living with them, in addition to many palpable joys and upsets, I had had an advantage, a continuing font of well-being, of which I had remained almost entirely unaware: I had lived among others who were plainly "inside" my life, plainly demarcated from the rest of the world. In them I had found, if not replacements for my parents, beings who could satisfactorily conceal from me the void I had created in my life by rejecting my parents. After Niki, Laura, and at last Philip had left, I found myself an orphan. Even though I had claimed to despise it, the idea of family turned out to have been my mainstay, or perhaps my crutch — in any event, the unadmitted assumption about my life that had allowed me to advance with a sense of security across the years, not to mention the Atlantic Ocean; so that, finding myself "alone", I sank into a despondency of utter helplessness. Needless to say, this experience of "abandonment" made my reconciliation with my mother and father at a later time all the happier. I trust as well that it allowed me to attend them in their last years aware of the curiously parental role a child assumes in its parents' eyes.

Teachers and Masters

My best teachers were also friends: teachers who became friends, friends from whom I was willing to learn. Ten years ago I first started teaching, and I found that being a teacher disposed me to accepting a role not superior but equal to the students I had to teach. Teaching implies a devotion to possibility for the tandem of teacher and taught in one and the same event. I hope that my own teachers shared the joy they gave me.

In grade school I had Captain Fry, whom I came to address as Humphrey after several years of savouring his distinguished South-English discourse. Tall and lean, a little sallow from having been gassed in the First World War, he presented himself to us as a figure of lanky, intense, somewhat otherworldly (or at least Old Worldly) elegance. He taught Latin and English, in the first subject relaying my grandfather's enthusiasm by nudging me through the hard grammatical years with hints and occasional samples of satisfactions to come; in the second, opening wide the doors of poetry through his eloquent advocacy of the Romantics and post-Romantics. I think he had almost no use for any poetry after Shakespeare and before Wordsworth, and this did me no harm, since my mother had exposed me to Milton with her incantatory recitations of "Lycidas," and her love of Marvell prepared my way for discovering the Metaphysical poets.

Humphrey Fry not only confirmed my hedonistic addiction to Keats and Shelley, he converted me, purely through a crafty exposition of his own rather superannuated taste, to the fascinations of Robert Browning. Indeed for several years I was a Browningite; neither a good thing nor a bad thing in itself, but in shifting my interest in poetry from its sensuous to its riddling, difficult, "intellectual" side, he prepared me for my later fascination with T.S. Eliot, through whom I would discover the domain of modernist writing. Humphrey Fry disliked Eliot and would surely have denied any connection between him and the affirmative Victorian whose work he revered.

One connection I later made had to do with Humphrey himself. He was imbued not only with Shakespeare but with the King James translation of the Bible. (I remember once, when a few of his students were summering with him in New England, his returning after a day's absence to find that we had left all the household chores undone, upon which he declaimed as we scurried for our hoes and brooms, "O generation of vipers, who hath warned thee to flee from the wrath to come?" I have done my chores conscientiously ever since.) The abundance of Biblical reference in Humphrey's speech made "Ash Wednesday", for instance, reassuringly familiar when I later came to it.

It was in one of Humphrey's English courses that I wrote my first poem, which began:

> It was a sad autumnal morn,
> The earth was but a mass of clay;
> Of foliage the trees were shorn,
> Leaving their branches dull and grey.

I remember covertly staring at him over my assignment book as he read my verses. When he finished, he gazed into the distance with a look that must have economically expressed two views: "What must happen will happen" and "My God, what have I done?" Masters at expensive schools are supposed to teach their wards the pleasures of reading poetry, but not perhaps the exhilaration of writing it.

After Pearl Harbor, my family moved to Washington, where my father, commissioned in the Naval Reserve, served in the intelligence department. As a result I was sent to a boarding-school a year sooner than expected; and so I found myself at Groton School in eastern Massachusetts, a place where I had no desire to go or, during the five years I spent there, to stay. After I had graduated, John Pick, a teacher who had left Groton to teach at Marquette University, wrote me this comment about the school: " . . . The mass conformity there is horrible and stupefying; possibly this is because everyone there lives so communally: and no one can be so tyrannical as the young: the refined and yet athletic bourgeois spirit is a terrifying combination." Theodor Mommsen, another mentor, who went on to teach at Princeton and Cornell, used to say that he had never seen a place where Christian charity was so much preached and so little practised.

If my life at Groton was often unhappy, it was by no means wholly so. In the first place, my class was a rather un-Grotonian one, full of brilliant, irreverent individualists. In the second place, the war had removed many members of the faculty to perform their patriotic duty, and the shortage of qualified teachers often led the school to hire in their place men very distant in background and temperament from the ideals of WASP Episcopalianism the school embodied. Among these replacements were Ernst Loewenberg, a Jew from Hamburg; Mommsen, another German, whose speciality was Petrarch and the Italian Renaissance; and Pick, a Roman Catholic, the author of the first book-length study of Gerard Manley Hopkins. These men brought to the cloistered and narrow-minded place a most welcome atmosphere of European culture, with its respect for art and intellectual distinction. To my regret I was never close to the extraordinary Ernst Loewenberg; but Pick and Mommsen both befriended me, and by the time they left, two or three years after I had come to the school, they had (with the considerable support, I should in fairness add, of such school regulars as Malcolm Strachan and Ned Gammons) radically expanded the frontiers of my mental life, and indeed kindled the curiosities that still sustain me during my working hours.

To John Pick I owe my discovery of modern poetry — not only Hopkins but Eliot, whose haunting musical lines bewitched and bewildered my melancholy adolescent reveries. (It was my passion for Eliot that later led me to other contemporary poets and also to Joyce and an extensive reading of Henry James.) John Pick, however, became far more to me than a literary counsellor. His almost impudent worldly urbanity put Groton's provincial gravity very stylishly in its place — a respectable place, but clearly not the only one where the good life could be led. He also proved to be a man of truly Christian kindness: I say this not in praise of Christianity, only as an indication of how obstreperous, demanding, and impatient I was. He dealt with my shortcomings firmly and attentively; the rest of the time he was all encouragement and useful entertainment — by which I mean a regaling fountain of information and even gossip, which was never just that, rather gossip disguising a parable from which I could not fail to learn because I could not fail to be amused. John Pick was witty and jovial and ruthlessly serious in his concern for me; and if at the time I didn't have the sense to recognise the seriousness through the delightful sparkle of its embellishments, I must have known it was there, because I never let go of him. After he left Groton, we at once began corresponding. I visited him in Milwaukee when I was at boot camp in Great Lakes; he visited us (with his late-wed Maltese-Florentine-Catholic aristocratic wonder of a wife) in Mallorca in the mid-fifties. During the latter visit I showed him my scanty but hard-worked-over work, and it was John, by sending my poems to William Alfred, who was responsible for my first publication — a poem called "The Pines at Son Beltran" that appeared in *Hudson Review* in 1956.

During my second year at Groton, while I was submitting to John Pick's rewarding influence, I contracted an even more remarkable debt to Ted Mommsen. Because I was his student, Ted was able to intervene in my life more directly than John. He was able to observe not only my general attitude towards school but how I actually worked. Because he too treated me with ruthless seriousness, he refused to accept me as he found me: someone who never consented or dared to do his best but was satisfied with getting slightly above-average, essentially mediocre grades. At the end of two months, Ted told me that he would no longer put up with my "laziness". Henceforth he would take ten points off any grade under 85, which was the lowest honours grade; furthermore, he intended to inform the faculty that I was for all intents and purposes a slacker and that he recommended pressuring me mercilessly until I did much better. I was outraged by this treatment; but outrage was of no use. (I should point out that I felt honestly victimised: I was truly unaware of being capable of more than I was doing.) My other teachers delightedly followed Ted's prescriptions, and escape quickly became impossible. I had no choice but to work harder. By the end of the year I was an honours student, one of the best in my class.

Ted did more than badger me into these results. As soon as he saw that I had begun to work seriously, he supplied me with the tools I most needed. He taught me how to read schoolbook if not scholarly texts; he taught me how to write papers and (blessed man) exams. What he showed me was simple, obvious, necessary: how to organise the subject at hand. In reading, this meant abstracting what one read and then realigning the skeleton of the text so that it was readily available (for writing exams, for instance). In writing, organising meant marshalling all one's knowledge of a subject and then giving it the same analytic and available form. I thus learned that in writing conceptual structure can lend incomplete, even inadequate material a convincing weight. After that, I never needed to pretend that I knew more than I did: whatever I did know usually proved more than sufficient for my needs. This has sometimes made of me an infuriating and slightly stupid conversationalist.

Outside of the classroom, Ted Mommsen talked to me about music, art, architecture, the literatures of Italy, Austria, Germany, and France, his life as a scholar. Ted to me exemplified the European humanist intellectual: cultivated, undogmatic, universally curious, gifted with a power of synthesis as great as his meticulousness in matters of detail. He left Groton a year or two before my graduation to teach at Princeton, where his presence was one of the main reasons I attended that college. Although we remained good friends, in time I lost touch with him, something I bitterly regret in view of his untimely death a few years later. Three decades have passed since then, and I still miss him, wishing he could read my stories and poems, wishing I could be sitting with him on some Renaissance piazza, learning where I was and who I was, wishing I knew someone able to reveal to me Petrarch, Stefan Georg, *The Abduction from the Seraglio*, and the painting of Sassetta.

After school, those I learned from were friends rather than teachers, although I had the privilege of studying under some prodigious intelligences: at Princeton, Blackmur, Rowley, and Gordon Craig; Cam, Piston, and Gombosi at Harvard. Emerging from the sheltered regime at Groton, however, did more than free me from certain Puritanical fetters: it cost me the intellectual passion that at school had provided me not only with a defence but with a way of distinguishing myself. The relief of escaping from a small, staring world allowed my curiosity to turn towards more ordinary social satisfactions. And in college my somewhat fierce schoolboy stances in cultural matters looked feeble: dozens at Princeton knew T.S. Eliot as well as I did and, furthermore, considered him old hat. I did have the luck (I cannot call it wisdom or even cleverness) to choose music as my major, so that throughout my college years I had to keep working hard to stay abreast of my courses in that most practical of the arts. Both at Princeton and at Harvard I learned harmony and counterpoint from young composers such as Elliot Forbes, Allan Sapp, and Robert Middleton, who transformed theory into a discipline of aesthetic discovery.

My choice of music was primarily founded on this crazy reasoning: since my overwhelming passion was for literature — for reading and writing it — I must take care to preserve that passion from the academic mind. So I took no courses in English literature. Luckily my precautions proved insufficient, because I did continue my grandpaternally-blessed study of Greek, and so found myself (with only two other students) spending a semester reading Greek tragedy with Eugene O'Neill, Jr., a powerfully imaginative explicator of texts so in advance of his time that I discovered no one comparable to him before the French post-structuralist critics of the following generation. If I remember correctly, his first class was entirely spent deducing the totality of *Oedipus Rex* from its first two lines, and doing this in so convincing a manner that the scope of reading was definitively transformed.

I did not become friends with O'Neill. I don't think I would have dared pursue that grand, capacious man, whose booming bass voice, more Russian than Irish, invested the antique lines he read with a solemnity both spellbinding and intelligent. Elsewhere the teachers who mattered most to me were those I saw mainly out of the classroom. Randall Thompson (he would later oversee my transfer to Harvard, where he himself had moved, "to be nearer," as Paul Henry Lang said, "the souls of his ancestors") not only helped me through my first courses in music but invited me from time to time to his house, where I became friends with his daughter Varney. With the other ladies present, she did much to wean me from my adolescent gaucheness. Even more helpful in ridding me of my old apprehensiveness was the poet William Meredith, with whom I studied writing for a year. He was a sympathetic and perceptive teacher, but our views of poetry were too far apart for me to learn what I might have from him: much a post-Audenite, he pursued a poetic "magic" compounded of charm and reasonable discourse, while I was still attached to the Eliotic mysteries of initiation and propitiation. Socially, however, Bill had everything to teach me, and if I did not learn everything, I developed an ability to survive cocktail parties lasting well past midnight, drinking martinis of ever increasing dryness with practically nothing to eat, in the company of men and women somewhat or more than somewhat my elders, and so far surpassing in wit anyone I had heretofore known that for once in my life I was satisfied to observe, pleased if I managed not to make a fool of myself before crossing the one or two courtyards that separated me from my spinning bed in Henry Hall. Thanks to Bill, I met my first young writers: Frederick Buechner, James Merrill, W.S. Merwin (to whose off-campus porch I sometimes repaired to listen to him converse with his GI-Bill, un-Princetonian fellow students about writing, art, and politics). Bill's gatherings, and Bill himself, brought me the blessing of reassurance about traits that at Groton (and in the WASPish New York that was the only one I knew) seemed peculiar. There was absolutely nothing wrong with having a passionate interest in Guillaume de Machaut, Henry James, late Beethoven quartets, or the woodcuts of Hokusai. My problem was no longer knowing more than my peers about such things, but so much less.

Friendships

Before the age of six, I found the world an easy, happy place to be. If it was mainly peopled by my parents and maternal grandparents (for whom I was an only grandson as well as an only son), I had no trouble including in it the boys and girls of my age with whom I played. When I reached six, this comfortable period ended. I have told myself that the reason for the change lay in my reaction to school (that crowd of others) or to the arduous process of becoming literate (when my mother tongue was taken away from me) or to some real or imagined event that I have suppressed. The only thing I am sure of is that at that age I and the world became two.

Until then I had been good-humoured and agreeable; I now became, at least in my own eyes, disagreeable, moody, and mistrustful. Although it would be overdramatising my life to say that between the ages of six and fourteen I had no friends at all (my older cousin Frank Cabot, with whom I have so happily renewed an affectionate relationship in recent years, was one constant if intermittent companion), I think back to that time as a systematically friendless one; and what was systematic about it was my determination to let no one close to me. I entertained an inconsistent attitude: no one should be allowed to see how basically vile I was, and no one could be trusted to appreciate me at my true value. The early and soon obsessive awakening of my sexuality (to use a vague term covering a multitude of urges and acts) strongly reinforced this attitude. By the time I was thirteen I felt that I had been condemned to prurient solitude, from which I prayed to be rescued some unforeseeable day by an incarnate goddess both sublimely romantic and unspeakably crude.

Patricia Ripley was beautiful, and perhaps with others romantic, but certainly not crude; rather, generous, perceptive, and full of mischievous wit. I met her during summer vacation in Maine in 1944. I trusted her because she too read and wrote poetry and liked to sing the poignantly remote music of the late Renaissance. I suppose she liked me because I made her laugh and because she could see in me not unappealing qualities of which I was desperately unaware. We never "dated", but we managed to see each other often, and in the course of that vacation Patricia allowed me to start realising that friendship could be something other than a trap to catch, possess, and eventually humiliate me. I liked her lively company so much that with her I forgot all my obsessive precautions. Thanks to her, I took my first steps in the direction of the men and women who would become the stuff and substance of my life.

My social education was continued during the ensuing months by a classmate at school, a genial, intense, soft-spoken Philadelphian named Bobby Scott, who even more mysteriously than Patricia chose to make me his friend. We had no particular tastes in common; indeed an element of his fascination for me was the competence he showed in domains I had never explored. He had a startling ability to sense what actually was going on in situations and relationships, so that through him I began to understand that there exists an active, practical intelligence distinct from that found in books and no less impressive. Almost alone in our class, he was well informed and acutely concerned about national and international politics, and through his example I discovered (by reading the *Nation* and the *New Republic*, for instance) that war-time patriotism did not supply answers to all public questions. Lastly, Bobby paid the most serious attention imaginable to the theoretical issues that arose in and out of the classroom — ethical, religious, philosophical — again providing me with an incentive to divert my attention from my dream-soaked head to the world around me.

But Bobby's chief effect on me lay elsewhere. By readily accepting me as his friend, not only keeping me company at school but, during vacations, travelling with me or inviting me to stay with his delightfully stylish parents, he encouraged me to wonder whether my character might not be the irremediable mess I had thought: his liking me encouraged me to like myself. Furthermore, the quality of his behaviour towards me gave me a first and best lesson in human relationships: from the start he relegated the "question" of our being friends to the category of assumed facts, thereby clearing the time we spent together for the fun of observation and improvisation. I wish I had been a better disciple; but I was too touched at having been singled out by this exceptional boy, and too grateful for his patience, to be able to accept myself as his equal — something I inevitably came to resent, so that in turn I felt justified in turning to less demanding (and less entertaining) friends.

Another boy with whom I was close at school and during my college years as well was Paul Bator. He was gifted with passionate charm and one of the most impressive intelligences I have ever encountered. He was also a fine musician; his enthusiastic advocacy of the classical and romantic repertoires, as well as that of Italian opera, did much to expand my severe taste, which tended to scorn everything between Palestrina and Stravinsky.

Paul had come to America from Hungary with his family in the late thirties. Through him I had my first inkling of the huge intellectual and cultural resources of that country, so small on maps, so large in its influence on the world. Much later, Paul was to introduce me to two other Hungarians, Ivan and Suzanne Waldbauer, professional musicians of great distinction (Ivan a genius of analysis and interpretation, Suzanne a superb performer). They revealed to me the world of music in its non-academic, practical guise, in addition to offering a kind of friendship I had not yet met with: pessimistic, frank, witty, open, and warm.

Paul Bator, the Waldbauers, and I shared a friend in Cliff Baum, whom I had known at Princeton through William Meredith. He had then brought into my life such quantities of fresh air that I was almost blown down by them. Through him I had my first glimpse of what at that time might have been described as Greenwich Villagedom: a world where social theorising, left-wing politics, psychoanalysis, and radical artistic enterprises mixed in a giddyingly glamorous and scary sexual/cultural free-for-all. The glimpse was useful in weaning me from my tiny gentility, but I hardly dared do more than watch.

At Harvard I had excellent companions; but it was not until I moved to Europe after my graduation that I found a friend who intimately affected my life. I had already met Anthony Bonner in 1944 and since then seen him occasionally. I knew him first as the son of family friends, then as a jazz musician, then as a classical composer. In 1951 he had come to Paris to study composition. When I looked him up, in the autumn of 1952, he and his wife Eve were living on rue Lincoln, off the Champs-Élysées. My wife, Niki, and I saw them more and more frequently. They came to visit us during the months we spent in the south of France, and after our return to Paris we rented a house with them. In the late summer of 1954 the four of us moved for an indeterminate stay to Mallorca, then tourist-free and thrillingly cheap. Tony and Eve are still living there. (Tony, after trying his hand at many trades, has become a world-respected authority on the greatest Mallorcan of all, the medieval philosopher and theologian Ramon Llull.)

Because of distance — Mallorca practically speaking is much farther from Paris than Los Angeles — I have seen little of Tony since the mid-fifties, but for four crucial years he was the friend with whom I made my way. He is perhaps the only friend of whom it can be said that I learned not only from him but with him: experimenting together with life in France, life in Spain, methods of musicianship, the works of Ezra Pound (whom we spent a year reading, collating by mail our interpretations of the *Cantos* between Palma de Mallorca and Deyá, ten miles away).

Tony intervened to extraordinary effect on certain occasions in my life: notably in giving Niki, at a critical moment, decisive support in her ambition to become an artist; soon after that in encouraging my own efforts when I started writing again. But essentially I think of Tony as someone with whom I was able to explore possibilities. When we became friends we were in our mid-twenties. I was riddled with doubts as to what I could or should do with my life. Tony's scepticism towards received ideas, towards everything the world and especially our parents' milieu felt entitled to expect of us, was of incalculable help to me. So was his patience, most strikingly his patience with himself. On the road to his present distinction he was willing not only to try out different ways of supporting his family but to devote exhaustive attention to whatever new subject attracted his interest — Villon, the Troubadours, higher mathematics — as though he had a truckful of lifetimes ahead of him. Whatever doubts he himself may have felt were never allowed to spoil these sustained exercises in learning. From his example I myself learned to take my time; and, where writing is concerned, never to settle for results that are merely reassuring.

During my two years on Mallorca I made a number of friends: Robert Graves (when we found a house to rent in Deyá, he turned out to be our neighbour), a difficult, demanding, restless man who proved more than kind to us — he and his wife Beryl accompanied the premature birth and early precarious months of our son, Philip, with not only sympathy but considerable practical help; the poet Alastair Reid, who with an abundance of good humour both encouraged my ambitions as a writer and kept them from making me (I had not yet published a line) altogether obnoxious; and finally Walter Auerbach, whom I met in Barcelona and persuaded to move to Deyá, where he spent the rest of his life.

In his late forties when I met him, Walter was a German Jew from Darmstadt who had left Germany in the early thirties and worked at many trades, among them filming news-reels in Palestine and photographing works of art in the United States. He had always worked as little as possible, his priorities being survival and pleasure. When I found him in Barcelona, he was surviving not only pleasurably but almost grandly on a U.S. Army pension of fifty dollars a month.

There and in Deyá he never failed to be well housed, well supplied in food and drink, and neatly dressed. He was rather tall and stocky; he had been bald from late adolescence, as a result of a nutritional malady during World War I; he had big eyes that he turned on people in an unscrupulously dramatic stare that produced an immediate reaction, whether of sympathy or mistrust.

After we moved to Mallorca, Niki and I adopted him, and he us. We gave him a family, in which he played a discreetly avuncular role. To us he brought a world of new culture: of Germany in the twenties — Brecht and Marxism, to simplify matters — and also of New York in the late forties and early fifties, distinguished by unheard-of painters such as Robert Rauschenberg and Jane Freilicher and remarkable young poets of whom the most remarked was someone named John Ashbery. Walter and I also used to share a passion for walking, spending many hours in the hills or on the little-motored roads of Mallorca's spectacular northern coast.

In the spring of 1956, Niki, Laura, and I visited Paris to start looking for a place to live when we moved back there. Walter joined us in May or June. In the course of his visit he arranged a meeting that would greatly affect my life. Walter had gotten in touch with John Ashbery, then a Fulbright scholar in Montpellier; and on a grey, warm afternoon, in a café on the Jardin du Luxembourg, I first spoke with an affable, apparently diffident, conventionally suited and cravatted man in his late twenties whose first collection had just been published in the Yale Series of Younger Poets.

I find myself hesitant, although hardly "at a loss", to describe my friendship with Ashbery. The friendship has been uninterrupted since our meeting, and throughout it John has shown himself (as with his numerous other friends) utterly tolerant and encouraging: an attitude that has allowed me to evolve in my relationship to literature and the world at large in progressions that only became apparent to me after they have occurred. The spur to my development has never come from injunctions on John's part, or even advice. (He is notoriously reluctant to make anything resembling a pronouncement on general issues, at least not in a serious vein.) If his witty discourse serves as a delightful, indirect medium for defining his preferences, it is above all his example as a masterly and, more impressively, as a dedicated artist that he exerts his influence on those around him; although even this statement too grossly ennobles the manner in which that influence works. Soon after we met I asked John what contemporary French poets he recommended I read. He mentioned several familiar names, such as Reverdy and Michaux. A week or two later, when I showed him a new poem I'd written ("The Battle"), he commented, "Oh, I see you've been reading those poets we were talking about." But I hadn't. Somehow the words he had said about them had given me a perception of their approach to poetry, and I had at once been able to incorporate this in my writing. A simple conversation with John had let me emerge from my conservative, provincial, and precious attraction to the kind of lyric poetry then being written in America and discover the possibility of "modernism" — a world where I was allowed and in some sense obliged to invent what I wrote.

John found me a provincial, very much on the defensive, reluctant to trust my own powers and tastes. Over the years he has greatly enlarged my views. In the domain of literature — especially by introducing me to the works of Raymond Roussel and by suggesting an unacademic and thoroughly exhilarating approach to Kafka — he started me on the way at last to writing fiction. (His detailed critique of *The Conversions*, after he read the first draft, provided me with the encouragement I needed then and during subsequent years of frequent incomprehension.) His then unlikely enthusiasms in film (the silent works of Feuillade and Lang; musical comedies; schlock horror movies), in painting (Ad Reinhardt), and in music (post-romantic composers like the still under-appreciated Busoni, as well as all that is most innovative in more recent music) saved me again and again from the most deadly of aesthetic fates: making final choices. And in exercising this liberating influence, John never for a day ceased being his generous and funny (and difficult and anxious) self. His unstinting readiness to be my companion in the early sixties, when the break-up of my marriage had left me depressed and lonely, still warms me with the memory of our evenings, our travels together.

One of our trips together brought us in (I think) November 1961 to Mallorca, where Walter Auerbach had arranged with a local printer to produce the first issue of *Locus Solus*, a magazine we were starting. John and Kenneth Koch had long wanted to create a vehicle for their work and that of friends they admired; for my part, I was discouraged by my initial failure to find a publisher for *The Conversions*. (Kenneth Koch would successfully propose it to Random House soon afterwards.) When I inherited a small legacy from my grandfather, John suggested I use part of it to pay for *Locus Solus*, where we could *all* be published. John and Kenneth asked James Schuyler to be a fourth editor. Over the next two years we brought out four issues of the review (one a double issue), the first printed in Palma, the others in Geneva.

John also opened up new social horizons to me. Through him I met around 1960 an incandescent galaxy of New Yorkers, thanks to whom my native city became a place where I felt at home: the painters Jane Freilicher, Larry Rivers, Alex Katz, Joe Brainard, and Ellen Adler (then married to David Oppenheim); writers, in addition to Koch and Schuyler, like Kenward Elmslie, Arnold Weinstein, and Bill Berkson; John's colleagues at *Art News*, Tom Hess and Betsy Baker. I have remained friends with most of them to this day. Later, it was through John that I came to know David Kalstone, Tomasz and Julita Mirkowicz, Joseph McElroy, and John Ash, all of whom much affected my life.

In the year following the end of my marriage I became friends with a young Englishwoman named Tina Packer, whom Niki and I had met on our return from Mallorca. In the spring of 1961, in a state of catastrophic disarray, I instinctively turned to her as someone of sufficient strength, compassion, and a wisdom beyond her years (she was almost a decade younger than I) to help me emerge from my despondency. Tina, then an ill-paid novice journalist, responded to my appeal with great tough-mindedness; and in doing so she established what has been one of the strangest as well as the most exuberant relationships I have known. For the next fifteen years Tina and I considered ourselves good friends, yet we scarcely ever saw each other. When we did, it was "only" because one of us was experiencing a gigantic crisis in his or her life. When Tina decided to leave her husband, for example, she drove straight from London all the way across France to Grenoble, where, half an hour from the village where I lived, she announced her urgent and imminent arrival with her infant son. A few years later, after my son, Philip, had run away from home, and two weeks of thinking and drinking had not reconciled me to the fact, I knew that my only hope lay in a visit to Tina. (She condemned me to a macrobiotic diet for a week, then sent me off to New York to raise money for her new theatrical enterprise, thereby replacing a set of impossible worries with another, more productive one.) I am happy to say that Tina and I now meet more frequently and in calmer circumstances, since she is settled in Massachusetts, where she is the artistic director of Shakespeare and Company (in Lenox) as well as of the Boston Shakespeare Company. Still, when the bottom falls out of the boat, both of us know where we can and probably must turn.

I have never had many friends in France, where friendliness or at least polite and discreet acquaintance rather than friendship is the rule. John Ashbery introduced me to a number of Parisians, some of them American artists (most notably Joan Mitchell and James Bishop), poets such as Denis Roche and Marcelin Pleynet, and his great companion Pierre Martory. After John returned to New York, I sought out and frequented a number of French writers, André du Bouchet and Maurice Roche in particular. It was indirectly through Maurice that I one day in 1970 received a letter from the thirty-four-year-old novelist Georges Perec.

Georges had written to me to express his enthusiasm for *The Conversions*, which he had just read in proof in its French translation. I answered his letter, and we soon arranged a meeting, which took place at the Bar du Pont-Royal, an agreeable place much frequented by writers and publishers. We drank together, and went on to have dinner, and I thus entered into the most exhilarating, hilarious, intense, and satisfying relationship I have ever known with a man, and doubtless will ever know.

I find it increasingly hard to write about Georges, who died five years ago of lung cancer at the age of forty-six. Two years after his death, when a Paris newspaper asked me to contribute an article about our friendship, this is what I wrote:

> Georges Perec wore a comic goatee that made him look like a silly scientist in the comics. His complexion was rough and peppered with warts. When I first met him he used to speak with one hand in front of his mouth to hide his disreputable teeth. Wiry hair swelled about his head like a disintegrating bird's nest. I often used Alcibiades' words about Socrates to describe him: a grotesque without, the golden image of a god within.
>
> I was wrong. I thought Georges looked funny; he *was* funny. He wore himself as his own mask. The mask revealed his unquestionable beauty, through eyes that were green, large, tender. It took me a while to realise that he was not someone to be liked but loved. After that, I loved him passionately.
>
> Literature can hardly explain such a passion. In our case it supplied a pretext for friendship and, later, the means of doing things on each other's behalf. What mattered to me in having Georges as a translator was not his talent or even (for one of my novels) his undertaking the work without any guarantee of publication, but his willingness to translate works that he had not

even read, simply because I had written them. More than literary sympathy, his collaboration was an assertion of loyalty. Whatever his motives in encouraging my election to the Oulipo, I know that he was happy that among its brilliant and tolerant members I at last felt at home in the country of my adoption. For his friends, Georges turned every opportunity that presented itself into an act of efficient generosity.

When we met, in 1970, our lives were at an ebb, professionally and privately. Georges was more obviously depressed; I maintained an air of confidence as though my life depended on it. In admitting his suffering, Georges was the wiser; and he admitted his friendship for me, too, while I dared not acknowledge how much I liked him. After all, I mistrusted no one as much as myself. Georges soon knew me better than I knew myself and taught me what friendship could be. With tact: knowing how Queneau's death would affect me, he made sure I learned of it from him, telling me the news coolly over the phone, even though the event was much harder for him to bear. With intelligence: through the years of intellectual "terrorism" he eloquently explained everything from Althusser to *S/Z*, never taking sides as he lured me out of dogmatic hypotheses.

He was famous for his wit, which was a defence against those he mistrusted and a spontaneous expression of gaiety among those he liked. His wonderful puns (*le phalle et la memelle*) were nourished by a boyish playfulness. There was childish enthusiasm too, in his taste for American films, which I particularly liked seeing with him since he teased and scolded me mercilessly for my Americanness. I remember the summer before he died seeing *Raiders of the Lost Ark* with him (in the afternoon — it was obviously a movie for hookey players): we enjoyed it like reading a new *Tintin*. Later, at a revival of

A Foreign Affair, our pleasures were not altogether shared ones. Georges was thrilled by the efficacy of Wilder's situations. I was touched more by the story itself: that of a moralistic American who learns in Europe the unsimple truths of history and passion, especially love. I was glad to see the film at Georges's side.

What can this friendship be called if not love? He attended with fierce intensity to those close to him (of whom I was only one: I said of him what Larry Rivers declared after Frank O'Hara's death, that he was my best friend, and forty others could say the same). Friendship with Georges was passionate love, and if ours because of our natures lacked the seal of physical involvement, I almost regret it, if only to know that nothing between us was missing. We did sometimes manage to "consummate our passion" in (again) a childish way: after dinner together, we would go home, lie on the living-room floor with a drink or a joint, and listen to somewhat "monstrous" works of music — *Tristan,* the Verdi *Requiem, Tommy.* Georges then reminded me of a faun or a bear cub, one that I would have longed to cuddle; but it was left to the music to supply our fleshly apotheosis. Afterwards we would give each other a hug and go our ways to bed.

Georges is dead. Of course his work in all its greatness remains. Unfortunately, it doesn't help.

(Published in *Le Monde,* July 27, 1984.)

The article on Georges Perec was written in the Venetian apartment (if so ordinary a word can apply to so ducal a dwelling) of David Kalstone, benefiting from his critical attention as well as from his hospitality; and different though David and Georges may have been in many ways, there is a certain appropriateness in speaking of one after the other. I met David in New York through John Ashbery, who had the good sense to introduce us on the eve of my moving to Venice. David had for four years spent his summers there, and it was in Venice that we came to know each other. David was nonetheless a thoroughgoing New Yorker, of the sort only those born elsewhere seem capable of becoming; and just as Georges articulated the mysteries of Paris literary and intellectual life in terms that I could grasp, so David generously came to be my interpreter of what was taking place in the world of American writing and publishing.

David Kalstone taught English literature, first at Harvard, later at Rutgers; he was an extraordinary critic, author of the best book I know on the poetry of Sir Philip Sidney as well as of a perceptive series of essays on modern poets. Good as his written work undoubtedly is, it hardly expresses the greatness of the man himself, even if it clearly illustrates one of his rarest qualities, one virtually extinct in our day: that of never allowing his penetrating intellect to outshine his even more penetrating sensibility. David's writings never draw the reader's attention to him, always to his subject, with an acuity that does not fear hiding beneath a harvest of bushels because it is so clear, confident, and perfectly focused; and as his innumerable friends will testify, this ready and concentrated attentiveness was marvellously available to them in all of their encounters with David, whether gossiping on the phone or evaluating a performance at the ballet or discussing a work of poetry, fiction, or criticism.

David combined absolute compassion with absolute independence of judgement; and lest that sound all too serious, he had a capacity for gaiety that was positively lowdown. He was constantly in touch with almost everything that seemed to matter to me — what was good or bad in my most recent work, how and where to get it published, how and where to get seats to a performance at the Met, or on Broadway, or off-off-Broadway, why Roland Barthes might usefully contribute to the cultural brew of 1983, why such-and-such a poet mattered, what poetry was, what art was, who had just gone to bed with *that* friend (and was he a real friend?), the delicious nuttiness of current political events.

What I chiefly learned from David was perhaps this: to relish everything that happens as the best possible entertainment and at the same time to take it with the utmost seriousness, for what else do we have? I'm afraid that he also, like Georges, taught me not to count on friends forever. Like Georges, he died before his time, a victim of AIDS. This is something to which I have not been able to reconcile myself in any coherent way.

An account of my friendships cannot be complete without at least mentioning a man who has had no connection with my activity as a writer (but he was the first to supply a "correct" explanation of the third riddle in *The Conversions*): Fred Warner, a British diplomat whom I met travelling in Egypt in 1963, when he was on leave from the Foreign Office. If I have left Fred to the end of this section, it is no accident. While I have enjoyed in the course of our visits and travels many facets of his High-Renaissance character (adventurousness, enthusiasm, worldly wiseness, melancholy, intellectual sophistication, fervent intelligence), I have also over the years acquired from him something I might have been more comfortable without: a notion of how the world really works. Such knowledge leaves no room for preconceived ideas, either of the left or of the right; so that now, almost equally dismayed by the dogmatic arrogance of the left and the unprincipled accommodations of the right, I have come to occupy an awkward political position, one consolingly close to Queneau's: that of not knowing the answers, remembering that this is no excuse for not asking the questions.

When I think of Fred, however, I don't think primarily of politics: rather of sitting with him in the shade of the Parthenon listening to him expound its magnificence down to the last shadow of a gilded shield; of hacking exorbitant brambles out of a stand of conifers on his Dorset farm; of striding hard after him as with Simone, Valentine, and Orlando I tramp through a primrose-studded wood overlooking England's once pirate-ridden southern shore.

Les femmes, les femmes, il n'y a qu'ça...

If I learned much from my teachers and more from my friends, I learned most from the women in my life: Niki de Saint Phalle, Anne Hollander, Élyette Héliès, Maxine Groffsky, Loredana Balboni, Marie Chaix.

I met Niki de Saint Phalle on summer vacation in the Berkshires when I was twelve. I saw her from time to time during the following years, usually at a distance, or at least distantly. One Saturday afternoon in the fall of my first year at college, I was addressed in the dining-car of the New York-Princeton train by a dazzlingly beautiful young woman whom I did not recognise, whom I at once pursued, and with whom several months later I eloped while AWOL from the Navy, whose disapproval was nothing compared to that of Niki's parents and above all my own. The step I thus took was not only rash but truly blind, and altogether salutary: I cannot imagine finding another way of breaking so emphatically and effectively with the world I had been brought up in, a world (whatever its virtues) that in 1949 offered me little hope of doing what I imagined I wanted to do. I hardly knew what the results of our initiative might be, and Niki knew no better than I; but where I had intermittent misgivings, Niki held doubts to be not only useless but irrelevant. What mattered was making the break, not what we would do after it. She supplied the determination to carry out our enterprise, rescuing me repeatedly from my quaint fear that if I turned my back on my family I would simply cease to exist. She showed me repeatedly that our life — which meant my life — was ours to create.

This determination of Niki's sustained me in many ways during our eleven years together. She was unwaveringly committed to life, to moving on, to discovering what lay around the next bend in the road. She manifested this determination in her hammer-and-tongs battle with my mother over having a child; in her ardent insistence on saving our marriage during the difficult summer of 1953; in her fidelity to her particular "primitive" gifts as an artist; in the tenacity with which she clung to her identity (and her life) after her health was ruined by hypothyroidism, and in the tenacity no less great with which, sick herself, she cared for our son, Philip, during his frightening childhood illnesses; in her witty, aristocratic confidence in my work as well as her own, a confidence all the more credible for the rare critical eye she turned on what I wrote; and finally, painfully, positively, in her willingness to end our marriage once she saw that the life had gone out of it and that preserving it so as to avoid suffering would mean betraying both of us.

She was right. We had married when I was nineteen and she eighteen: our marriage had given us a context in which to finish growing up, and now that we were at least potential adults, new contexts for new kinds of growth were in order. At the time, I was far too attached to our marriage to see this. Marriage had become the sheltering family without which I secretly believed I could not survive. Niki's departure left me in a state of recurrent gloom whose surface symptoms would require almost two years to be cured and whose less obvious, more pernicious effect — a paralysing reluctance to risk loving or being loved — would stay with me for well over a decade.

I know now that this condition was nobody's responsibility but my own. Niki may have left, but even then, and for all but a few months of the ensuing time, I was provided with good reasons *not* to feel abandoned. During the break-up itself I had met Anne Hollander, an American who was warm, generous, bright, elegant, charming, and pretty enough to have consoled Orestes bereft and enraged. Unfortunately, except for transatlantic visits, our romance had to be consummated in letters. She was married, by no means unhappily, and there was no question, in spite of our passion, of our devoting ourselves to one another. (If there had been such a prospect, I myself would have probably thought it a kind of sacrilege, after eleven years of strenuous conjugality.) Yet the time we managed to spend together was uniquely precious to me. Anne taught me that my rekindled yearnings for a relationship uniting tenderness and intense sexuality could exist outside of my reveries. Furthermore her epistolary genius showed how powerful the written word could become when animated by love. Her letters mattered to me more than any book, but they surely mothered *The Sinking of the Odradek Stadium*.

I was then spending almost all my time in Paris, where I had moved back with my children from Lans-en-Vercors, the mountain village where we had lived as a family for the two previous years. I was without Niki, without Anne, brooding compulsively over my less-than-unique fate, looking after Laura and Philip with distracted inconsistency. It was in these circumstances that I had a year-and-a-half-long affair with a Frenchwoman slightly older than I named Élyette Héliès. She was tough, sharp, experienced, no respecter of persons or of anything else, except for her friends and, fortunately, her lovers. In so far as it was possible, she weaned me from my well-meaning wishful thinking about the ways of the world, and she did so with a kind of merciless geniality that was inspired more by what she saw as a waste of my energies than by a desire to score points. Her teachings were grounded in her fidelity to the present, to what was actually happening at any given time; there was not a day I knew her when she was not willing to hazard our relationship, her possessions, her job, her comfort, anything apparently worth saving, if it conflicted with her intensely felt sense of what was fitting for the moment. She lived uninterruptedly at risk and clearly did so not out of a taste for recklessness or conspicuous individuality but with a confident, perhaps bitter wisdom that I willingly trusted, even if I could not begin to understand it. With Élyette, I felt that I was being driven by a nonchalant, expert driver at exhilarating speeds over unmapped roads. The landscape going past would never look the same again.

My time with her (and with Anne, too) came to an end when I made a trip to New York in May 1962. I rented an apartment on West Thirteenth Street for an entire month, the longest I had ever stayed in the city on my own. The publication of *The Conversions* was the occasion for my visit, and I had been looking forward to it, having not yet learned what disappointments such an event can bring. Although the novel made scarcely a public ripple, friends like Jane Freilicher and her husband Joe Hazan responded so enthusiastically to it that disappointments were forestalled; and I had meanwhile been given satisfaction of an altogether different sort. The editing of *The Conversions* had been done at Random House, with a skill and tact I appreciate to this day, by Berenice Hofmann and Maxine Groffsky. I corresponded with these editors at length, so that by the time I arrived in New York I felt on friendly, almost intimate terms with them. Where Maxine was concerned, the intimacy soon became fact.

Maxine was a woman of Olympic and no doubt Olympian prowess in looks, charm, energy, intelligence, and wit, imbued with a sexual candour that might have made her a winning fourth in the contest for Paris's apple. (It is foolish to say "was"; she is still capable of precipitating a four-lane pile-up.) Endowed with irreverent frankness balanced by good nature, with a caustic, rather cynical sense of realities that only makes her affections more convincing, capable of sustained anger and devotion, Maxine brought into my life a presence that was entire, powerful, and demanding. Maxine was challenging in many domains. She was as inspiring a dancer as she was an editor, she had incredible artistic flair, with a phenomenally perceptive ear and eye and a capacity for zeroing in on the critical heart of whatever was at issue whose only possible drawback was its speed — I sometimes felt like taking at least one breath before having to confront such superbly definitive judgements. As a result, during the eleven years we spent together, I learned to love dancing (and to watch it, too, especially Merce Cunningham and Ballanchine, those last great twentieth-century masters); I learned how to edit my own writing and came to read the work of others, such as James Salter, Dallas Wiebe, and Keith Cohen, that I might otherwise have regrettably missed; I discovered at least some of the lively things that were happening in American painting and sculpture; and, in general, I was cheerfully obliged to recognise the world around me as a place for discovery and communication, rather than the realm of a vaguely hostile otherness that I kept stubbornly conceiving it to be. Maxine brought openness, possibility, and generosity into my life. I was, foolishly, not ready for so much.

I made two mistakes, or what now look to me like mistakes, even if at the time I felt I could not act otherwise: I should have married Maxine, or I should not have taken her away from New York. If Maxine had stayed in New York, where she led a brilliant social and professional life, we would have had a very different kind of relationship, one that probably would not have left me with my present sense of opportunities squandered. Since Maxine came back to France with me, to live for eleven years in a country whose language and ways were as yet largely unknown to her, I should have committed myself definitively to her well-being. Fifteen years later I would not have hesitated to do so; but I was then pathetically enthralled by the dread of what my first marriage had ultimately brought me: the "unbearable" pain of its ending. I had been totally committed to Niki, and I had suffered for it. I wouldn't be caught in that trap again. Thanks to such reasoning, I stifled my capacity for love and denied myself what would have made me happiest. Maxine patiently put up with me as long as she could, and no doubt longer than she should have. I knew periods of great happiness with her; and at the end of each one of them I insisted perversely on turning back to a condition of what I had the presumption to call independence. Because both she and I have since dealt more justly with ourselves, the consequence of my attitude was less than disastrous — waste, not ruin; but what a waste!

Maxine went back at last to New York late in the winter of 1974. A few months later I moved to Venice, where I was to live for a little more than two years. Soon after my arrival, I met and at once fell under the spell of a Venetian unlike any woman I had known: Loredana Balboni, a paragon of loveliness, elegance, sweetness, hospitableness, and cultivation. Lest these words make her sound too good to be interesting, I can say that she is also a tough and agile art dealer and, in her personal life, capable of quite irresistible gaiety.

I was quickly enchanted by Loredana, and I found myself drawn as well to the social pleasures of life under her roof. I became an almost disreputably constant guest at her table and in her drawing-room. I underwent a fascinating apprenticeship in the life of a certain stratum of Italian society that is hard to identify, since it included, as well as writers and artists, professional men and businessmen and an occasional politician. Loredana watched over my successes and my gaffes among her guests with a reassuring, fond serenity. And when the cold and darkness of winter emptied the city of visitors, she filled up her salon with her own genial radiance: so that the evenings spent alone with her came to be those I by far preferred — they came to seem my special rewards for having not too disgracefully survived the more arduous social occasions. In the course of those evenings à deux I learned to benefit from my friend's knowledge and experience, listening raptly to her accounts of her extraordinary and not too happy life.

I know that explaining relationships is a dubious if tempting exercise. Loredana's feelings about me were subdued by what I thought of, perhaps egotistically, as an essential dread of happiness. As a young woman she had been married twice, to two exceptional men; both had died. Did these experiences lead her to recoil from yet another serious attachment? For the first time since Niki's departure I was beginning, in Loredana's presence, to feel capable of making such a commitment myself. She herself spoke of the possibility warmly enough. At the same time I felt that I was never allowed into the most intimate circle of her thoughts and choices, no matter how much openness and kindness she showed me.

Then, during a visit to New York in the fall of 1975, I was offered the job of translating a recent French novel, a book unknown to me, although it had, during my Venetian absence, been a best-seller in France: *The Laurels of Lake Constance*, written by a woman in her early thirties named Marie Chaix. The novel was thoroughly autobiographical, describing the life of Marie Chaix's father during his politically appalling career as a high-ranking member of the Fascist *Parti populaire français*.

I agreed to translate the book because at first glance I assumed that it would be easier than the avant-garde work which had provided me with my previous experience of translation. *The Laurels* proved much harder and also much more affecting than I expected; in fact it overwhelmed me. Having read it through twice and started on the work of translation, I wrote the author (her discreetly alluring photograph adorned the book's cover) a letter that I hoped would lead to a more than ordinary acquaintance. I used every writer's trick I knew to make myself interesting; and when I had finished the letter, I tore it up. I realised that the author of a book so intensely felt and so compassionate deserved better than a disguised come-on. I composed a new, short letter, courteous and respectful, sent it off to Marie Chaix, and relegated my fantasies to the Venetian fog.

On receiving this second, respectable letter, Ms. Chaix, mother of two and until then a resolutely devoted spouse, almost left her family to pay me a visit in Venice. It was as though my first letter had been encrypted in the second one — an interesting lesson in the workings of language. Six weeks later I had my first conversation with her, by phone, mostly about her book; but much else happened during that hour-long talk, and not entirely in my imagination, because when we finally met two weeks after that, neither I nor Marie could long entertain any doubt that something new, challenging, "impossible" had come into our lives; and, except for necessary separations, we have never left each other since.

It is hard to sum up what I have learned from Marie, with whom I have lived through the most trying and most productive time of my life, and from whom I am constantly learning. When we met, she offered me that opportunity of making myself wholly available to a woman towards which I had been slowly moving since the collapse of my first marriage; and available not only to herself but to her two daughters, then aged two and seven, who with their mother have given me a second family that has filled my days with new life. There is no greater satisfaction than that of being useful to others, except that of being useful to others one already loves: Marie, Émilie, Léonore.

Marie is also a writer (I had sworn never to live with a writer), and a French writer, and a writer whose practice in no way resembles mine. Showing perfect respect for my own concerns, she has revealed to me possibilities in writing that I might never have discovered; and what is true of writing applies to the rest of my life. Through her I have been able to see that my parents, my children, my cousins and my cousins' cousins, and friends long unseen and those freshly made, are the substance of my life: that my life is what I have and what I can make of that, not some wishful hope of what may (and doesn't) happen. She has demonstrated what happiness is without ever telling me what it should be.

It is now close to eleven years that Marie and I have lived together. Knowing her has not changed me: I am no less distracted, dilatory, self-indulgent, or confused than I was before. But there is not an hour in which, aware of and I trust responsible for my failings, I cannot subsume them in my intention of continuing to live with her to the end of my counted days.

Listening, Then Reading, Then Writing

One of two recollectable beginnings:

During several years of my childhood, I would go into my father's room most mornings and sit on a stool on the threshold of his bathroom while he shaved. Shaving for my father was a long, carefully executed rite, one that provided ample time for story-telling; and every morning my father, between prudent swipes at his chin, would slowly enunciate a new episode of whatever fabulous tale he was in the process of telling me. (In the evenings he would draw masterly illustrations of the stories.) I can't remember the first tale — perhaps one that involved crossing the isthmus of Panama, as a hilarious drawing of the world's greatest seaworm suggests. I know that when I was around six or seven we took trips to the moon and to Madagascar (where tribal rivals set the lanky N'Gombos against the pudgy Bambos).

Perhaps my father derived his narrative skill from his Kentucky grandfather, Basil Duke, on whose knee he had sat and listened to accounts of the Civil War. In any case, the only talent I feel I possess is that of telling stories, and clearly those fifteen-minute morning sessions with my father taught me what story-telling is about: beyond provoking the question "And then what happened?" digging the Procrustean bed from which that question can be reborn new every time.

The other beginning:

Aged eight or nine, I am walking with my mother westwards across Seventy-second Street, climbing the hill between Second and Third Avenues. Near the top of the hill, responding no doubt to some remark or question I have just uttered, my mother stops, turns to me, and says

> "O for a beaker full of the warm South,
> Full of the true, the blushful Hippocrene,
>   With beaded bubbles winking at the brim,
>   And purple-stainèd mouth;
> That I might drink, and leave the world unseen,
>   And with thee fade away into the forest dim."

My mother and father had read poetry to me — Stevenson's *Child's Garden of Verses*, some delicious poems of Kipling ("And the steward falls into the soup tureen...."), and Tennyson, who had given me my first moment of poetic wonder: "The splendour falls / On castle walls / And snowy summits old in story . . ." But not until my mother recited those lines of Keats did I know that poetry was a life-and-death matter, capable of arresting in her busy stride one of the two central divinities of my world, of bringing tears to her eyes, of evoking a vastness of longing and regret and desire altogether surpassing the words she was so deliriously letting fall from her so-strangely-lipsticked original mouth.

A couple of years later, at the bottom of the same hill, on the opposite side of the street, I saw in the window of (perhaps) a stationery store a book attractive enough to draw me inside, where I spent a respectable portion of hoarded allowance in buying it. The book was *Tom Sawyer*. It had an intriguing cover that showed Tom painting the fence in front of his envious friends. I had never heard of Tom or Huck or Mark Twain. I might have read and liked the book anyway, but having bought it gave reading it a special relish.

(This event is confused in my memory with the purchase of another book at the same store: a Pocket Book, then the only paperback available. When I proudly announced that I had bought myself a pocket book, glimmers of is-my-son-gay anxiety visibly troubled my mother's gaze until I made clear what I was talking about. The book wasn't *The Constant Nymph*, although I particularly remember reading that in the Pocket Book edition, but certainly later, during early adolescence.)

Meanwhile I was exposed to more poetry at school and duly swooned at some of it, Shelley's "Invitation", for instance — no: I discovered that for myself, in a slightly trashy book about Trelawny that wasn't trashy enough, since I expected romantic sex from it. Humphrey Fry began expounding his enthusiasm for Browning, turning me curiously into a century-late Browningite snob. There are worse fates for inexperienced proto-proto-writers, who are at least led to ask such questions as: is poetry a simple vehicle for complicated thoughts, or is it a complicated vehicle for simple thoughts?

I read lots of prose as well, although without, I think, the hope for the transformational, redemptive power I attributed to poetry. After *Tom Sawyer* I devoured all its sequels. Some time after that I binged on Noel Coward and Bernard Shaw. In between I regularly bought *Action Comics*, *Detective Comics*, and others whose names I've forgotten, although I shall never, ever forget Submariner, The Human Torch, or The Flash. The book that most affected me in the last years of grade school was *Out of the Night*, by a former German communist who took the name Jan Valtin: in it I learned about Hitler's concentration camps and their anti-Semitic horrors.

In adolescence reading took on a new virtue. I was in the midst of my "friendless" stage; books became my friends, and better than friends because my communion with them wholly depended on my willingness to lose myself in them, to take them seriously, to think and dream about them. They were my link with humanity, and with my own humanity, in which I hardly dared otherwise believe.

Not only reading offered me this refuge, but my own poetry. From the age of thirteen to seventeen I deemed myself happiest when I could be alone in the mudbath of language. I can't claim it was much more than that for me, although I was bright and soon well trained enough to appreciate and appropriate certain elements of abstract thought. The glory of language, however, for me had to include not only the mind but the rest of the nervous system as well, which it fed and consoled for its foolish but intense anxieties.

Just as a glutton desires more food than he needs, and eats more food than he desires, I heaped my life with books. Not only books to read but to own. Each new volume on my shelves added a brick to my defence works, the culture castle in which some day I hoped to live safely and alone (except perhaps for my sexpot goddess). I read as much as I could, well over a hundred books a year, but my craving for new acquisitions outstripped my reading. Eventually I came to realise that the prospect I was creating for my future (a lifetime of reading or of *not* reading, since one lifetime would hardly suffice) was more depressing than reassuring, and I gave up buying books systematically. To this day, however, the sight of a book catalogue can give me an almost pornographic twitch.

During those teenage years I read a great deal of modern poetry: after Eliot came Marianne Moore, Frost, E.A. Robinson (I voluntarily concocted a forty-page analysis of *Tristram*), and others to whom I was led by Louis Untermeyer's anthology. Eliot also pointed towards Donne and Marvell; in school I read Shakespeare and Milton. I have forgotten most of the fiction I read — I couldn't now identify a single situation in *The Rise of Silas Lapham* or *Giants in the Earth*. I read most of Hawthorne and Melville, *The Red Badge of Courage*, the incomparable *Walden* (still to me an exemplar of writing as a complete art), and such books left with me a lasting sense of their particular worlds, Hawthorne perhaps most of all: his bleaker moments may have appealed to me (as *Ethan Frome* certainly did) as reflections of my own little midwinter-New England melancholy, which I sought to express in the poems I wrote during my long months away from home.

I arrived at Princeton aspiring to become a poet. For the first year I continued to write, although less than before, and after that even less, and at the end of a year and a half not at all. This absence of not only the ability but the desire to write lasted until after my graduation from Harvard, from which I concluded that American college life was to blame for it. I may not have been wrong, but it no longer matters, and even then I never took what I imagined to be a permanent loss as tragedy. The Navy, marriage, fatherhood (the enthralling presence of Laura), the study of music, the prospect of Europe provided a full enough life. The loss also felt like what it was: an unwished-for renunciation that had left me stranded in a desert of unformulated questions.

In Paris, in 1952, Niki studied acting, to which she brought her beauty, dramatic instinct, and determination, and I conducting, to which I brought knowledge, enthusiasm, and an insurmountable lack of ear training. The following summer our still very young marriage endured a crisis. At the end of it Niki had a pseudo-suicidal nervous breakdown that allowed her, while she was being treated in a clinic in Nice, to rediscover her passion for art, and to discover her gift for it. When she then renounced the seductive, real prospects of an acting career to embark on her ultimately spectacular but then pathetically uncertain life as a painter, I watched her transformation with growing jealousy. And not only jealousy: with a sense that she had begun an existence that was all possibility, something like the possibility that I had guessed at in my poetry-making days at school. I started writing again.

I had the best imaginable partner in my undertaking, because Niki had once again no doubts about the life she had chosen. She welcomed me fervently into my belated resumption of an activity commonly called "creative", in any case one that depended wholly on its solitary practitioner. I picked up, I suppose, where I had left off years before; several more years would be necessary before I wrote a poem that I would keep, and it was not until my meeting with John Ashbery that I became conscious of what I might do, which is to say anything I wanted. Until then I remained conscientiously and not unrewardingly stuck in a kind of respectable neo-imagist exploration. I learned during this time the habit of relentless rewriting, something I came to rely on when I began working in prose.

Niki was also an acute reader. She insisted that I not miss what she recognised as great: Proust, Dostoevsky, Ford Madox Ford, *Oblomov*, Walter de La Mare's *Memoirs of a Midget*. (She also saved me the trouble of reading works like Roger Martin du Gard's *Les Thibauts*.) Niki was the first person I relied on to fill the gaps in my own reading; the others were Ashbery, Perec, and Marie Chaix. To Ashbery I owe my acquaintance with Roussel and Firbank and, as I've said, Kafka freshly read; to Perec, Flaubert; to Marie Chaix, Bruno Schulz, Colette, Marcel Schwob, and (perhaps the best of the four) Marcel Blecher.

In 1956 I began a novel, not knowing what to do. I tried to somehow elevate events in my life to the self-contained intensity of fiction. I still admired Albert Camus and half-heartedly half-took him for a model, managing one chapter that was at least readable, a second chapter that was at least finished, then a few aimless pages. It was like going to college all over again. The crises in Poland, Hungary, and the Middle East interrupted my efforts. Meanwhile I had begun reading Roussel: a hard task, one that at first amused me, then convinced me that Roussel was a thoroughly nutty eccentric, until I at last emerged on the vast, coldly illuminated plateau of his sovereign genius.

Reading Roussel brought me several revelations. He demonstrated to me that psychology was a dispensable fashion, that the moral responsibilities of writing did not lie in a respect of subject matter, and that the writing of prose fiction could be as scrupulously organised as Sir Philip Sidney's double sestina. Roussel taught me that I did not have to write out of my "experience" (the quotation marks indicate: what one thinks one has been able to avoid); that I had the universe to play with, not merely the pieties of a late-capitalist society; that writing could provide me with the means of so radically outwitting myself that I could bring my hidden experiences, my unadmitted self into view. I have sometimes felt that the aim of Roussel's imperturbable and arbitrary procedures was to supply the truths of paradox (such as "life after death") with the unchallengeable evidence of tautology (make a machine to revive the dead and they will "by definition" show signs of life). Such a project suggested that his methods were powerful and original enough to accommodate my own, as yet undiscovered ambiguities. That Roussel's procedures were based on word-play did not surprise me unduly. Who in my own country wrote more cunningly than S. J. Perelman, standing in for James Joyce on a package tour through supermarketed America? With Roussel I found myself in a familiar, wholly man-made landscape, where linen-and-thread baby's-breath smelled of real babies: the landscape of our reinventable, startling world. And if Perelman shrugged off his sometimes nightmarish fantasies with a public smile, Roussel stared at them with the unpainted gaze of a sea-washed statue of antiquity — one whose nakedness had been distractingly reclothed in strict turn-of-the-century costume.

In 1958, after we had moved to Lans-en-Vercors in the French pre-Alps, I began another novel, at first called *Invitation to a Sabbath*, later *The Conversions*. To the writing of this book I brought my Roussellian enthusiasm for freely and puzzlingly inventing new things to write about, as well as an ear entranced by Roussel's frighteningly, provocatively, movingly neutral voice. For my central subject matter I turned to my experience of Robert Graves's life and work, especially *The White Goddess* (almost as liberatingly strange as Roussel himself). The time I had spent with Robert had produced mixed feelings about him, if unmixed agreement with Eric Linklater's dictum that wanting to meet a writer because one admires his work is like wanting to meet a goose because one likes *foie gras*. (The dictum rings unfairly in my ears, because of Robert's kindness to me, for which I remember him affectionately. I remember too his admirable fund of knowledge: he was the first European I knew at all well who put my exaggerated intellectual assurance in its proper place. For some time to come, graduates of Oxford and the École supérieure des lettres are going to continue to make most of us look like promising freshmen.)

The White Goddess and Robert's ancillary writings on the subject, together with his rather goofy applications to life of his doctrine of the ninefold Muse, provided me with material for a story, which I reoriented to the history of witchcraft as I reimagined it after readings in Baissac, Michelet, Lea, and of course Margaret Murray. All these preparations, Roussellian, Gravesian, and witchy, provided fuel to the hypnotic passion with which I wrote the book: a passion that resembled less that of a romantic poet oozing inspiration through the tip of his pen than that of a shoemaker making boots for a queen. Because of certain reactions to my novels, I would like to add that the bootmaker's passion excluded indifference and ridicule. I and the "I's" telling my stories are never free of the stresses of emotion; but the "I's" and I know we are bootmakers, or only sandalmakers, throttled (not inexpressively for an attentive reader) by a restraint producing a kind of anguish-ridden understatement. We leave it to described events, to told stories, to do our speaking for us.

When I wrote *The Conversions* I was leading a happy life; a precariously happy one, it turned out. By the time I began *Tlooth* Niki had left, my life felt blackened. My second novel taught me that writing one book never makes the next one easier. Everything I set down had to be rewritten, not merely revised, and after that there was more rewriting to do. Maxine Groffsky patiently showed me ways that helped bring the intricate work to completion. Intricate, because so much of the religious underpinning of the book, recognisably close to the surface in *The Conversions*, was here mostly shoved out of sight. Combining the imperatives of this hidden subject matter with those of an adventure story whose main characters had to be kept sexually ambiguous, and inscribing the result in acceptable English sentences, often proved discouragingly difficult.

This is not the place to explore at length the reasons for the indirect, elaborate, and apparently frustrating approach to experience to which I resorted in my three first novels. In my opinion, which is no more than that, I was preoccupied with the problem of knowledge: what it is, how it can be communicated, and also what it is not and how it is often belied. Certainly the three books' cargo of cultural junk — historical, theological, and so forth — confirms this opinion; in that all the cultural constructs eventually go up in smoke, are shown to be misleading, or meaningless, or to mean things other than they claim. In *The Sinking of the Odradek Stadium* I pushed this approach to what I hope is its limit. The religious substructure — in the narrative it appears in the wedded opposition of a lapsed Roman Catholic and an efficient Buddhist — was complicated by projections of a future society, by painstaking accounts of economic and political life in medieval Florence, by a slightly loony application of the rules of the Big Con to a scholarly treasure hunt, to name only the more visible constraints. The problems I set myself were so daunting that I sometimes resigned myself to setting them down without finding their solutions — a recourse that hardly makes for easy reading. I was almost surprised when the book was finally published (thanks to Maxine and Fran McCullough) and gratified that it was so well received critically, at least in some pleasantly conspicuous places. I had become in the course of writing the book much attached to my two odd-ball spouses, and I was happy to have secured their love story a niche in the public world.

Waiting to find a publisher — *The Sinking* survived twenty-five rejections — I hesitated to begin another novel. If the best I had been able to do provoked such reluctance, why undertake another lengthy project? I wrote shorter fiction, poetry (*Trial Impressions*). and a book including both poetry and prose, *Selected Declarations of Dependence*. This last work was based entirely on a set of forty-four proverbs, which I exploited in terms of vocabulary, structure, and subject matter. This curious and demanding project was the result of my membership in the Paris-based group of writers and intellectuals known as the Oulipo.

The Oulipo — the *Ouvroir de littérature potentielle*, or Workshop of Potential Literature — was founded in 1960 by Raymond Queneau and his friend François Le Lionnais. Queneau was not only an outstanding novelist and poet but a practising mathematician; Le Lionnais was a chess expert and a mathematical historian; and at the outset the Oulipo's declared purpose was to apply mathematical structures to writing. The notion of mathematical structure was later expanded into that of constrictive form, a "constrictive form" being one that makes inescapably strict demands on the ingenuity of its user: a form rigorous enough to oblige anyone who uses it to say what he might never otherwise have said, and certainly not in the way he would normally say it. A constrictive form can be as rudimentary as a snowball or as complex as Queneau's *100,000 Billion Poems* (a set of ten sonnets that through permutations can produce that astronomical figure). What all constrictive forms have in common is the satisfaction they offer of meeting impersonal obligations.

Cursory descriptions of Oulipian activities and attitudes almost invariably lead to reactions such as: it sounds interesting and amusing but you're really just playing games. If Queneau, Calvino, and Perec like playing such games, who could help wanting to join the team? However, that is not how the Oulipo works. Writing, in the sense of producing works, is not its true concern. Meeting once a month for a working lunch or dinner of great and irreverent liveliness, the Oulipo supplies its members with a forum in which to explore the *potentialities* of the novel and the poem, or the paragraph and sentence, in terms of constrictive form and its consequences. It is a kind of laboratory of structural studies (it has nothing to do with structuralism, by the way). Later, or elsewhere, its members may choose to avail themselves of Oulipian methods in their work. That is their business, not the Oulipo's, which only formulates procedures and at most supplies minimal examples to clarify them.

My own near-Oulipian tendencies were well established before I even heard of the group, to which Perec introduced me in 1972. I have ever since rejoiced at having been co-opted into that unique body; but it is hard to say how much it has influenced what I subsequently wrote. The support of its members is certainly influence of a kind. I would prefer to say that the Oulipo has empowered me to reach what I was already struggling towards; by clarifying and expanding my awareness of what I was doing, it has enabled me to move towards what I had not yet done.

A description of the first section of *Selected Declarations of Dependence* may illustrate what I mean. I there set myself the task of writing a story using only the vocabulary of the forty-four proverbs on which the whole book is based. The task proved hard: the number of words at my disposal was less than two hundred. I had no idea of what to say, of what I might say. I found myself during my writing hours literally obliged to start living inside a world circumscribed by my chosen vocabulary. I began by saying possible things, writing them down, and comparing them. Little by little, possibilities of events appeared, and then links between the events. In time situations were created, although hardly by me. At least that is how I felt: I was becoming the medium for some unsuspected and strangely inevitable whole — as though in the course of a long walk I had stumbled into a valley full of dreamed trees, fissures and dancers. The story in the end "told itself". It was perhaps not the only story that could have evolved from that material, but it was certainly the only story I could then write in those circumstances. It was a story furthermore that I would never otherwise have written. The apparently arbitrary constraint that I had agreed to comply with turned out to be the means of unlocking an unsuspected cupboard of knowledge, so that I was able to make pages altogether fresh out of some of the most worked-over words in the language: as though I had constructed, like some genial castaway, a pleasure pavilion out of the worn pebbles edging the deserted beach where I had been stranded.

Many writers will recognise in this account a most familiar experience. From this I would conclude that Oulipian practice, seemingly extremist, provides a useful way into the central domains of writing or, more accurately, of the act of writing.

It may be all too easy to see the work I did in the years before starting *Cigarettes*, my much-postponed last novel, as preparation for it: *Selected Declarations of*

Dependence as an Oulipian workout; *Trial Impressions* (perhaps my favourite among my books) as an experiment in discovering how formal pretexts lead into intimate experiences; the translation of three autobiographical books — one by Perec, two by Marie Chaix — as an apprenticeship in applying the imagination to past personal events; the subsequent translation of Jeanne Cordelier's devastating memoir of her life as a prostitute (*La Dérobade*) as a lesson in writing colloquial, intensely felt dialogue. If at the time I could not have foreseen how these projects would contribute to a new novel, it is undeniable that they gave me an excellent training for writing it. I knew, long before *Cigarettes* was conceived of, that my next book would have to realise my desire to express in fictional transformations particular experiences of childhood, parenthood, friendship, and love. The stories the book tells have little enough to do with the events of my life. At the same time, those stories could not have been told if I had not looked for material, rather than in imagination giving substance to the ambiguities of language, in imagination giving substance to the ambiguities of remembrance. The distinction may be only an illusion, but the illusion ultimately provided a constraint absorbing enough to produce a book.

Leaving and Returning, Living and Dying

During the writing of *Cigarettes*, my life underwent a number of changes, some apparently superficial, some less so, that now strike me as corresponding to a shift in my attitude towards myself and towards the world. I would say that in general the focus of my life shifted from what I could learn by experiment to what I could learn by commitment, although I hasten to add that the first demand of commitment is to make the most frightening experiment of all: that of giving up what one already has. I surrendered my mistrust of others and accepted my relationships with the men and women I loved. I agreed to work with others in questioning the nature of life, of my life. I returned to my family: I reclaimed my mother and father as my mother and father. Each year I spent more time in the country and city of my birth. I started to teach. I started to write about myself. Out of these changes new relationships were born, and in the midst of the changes familiar relationships ended in death. So circumstances confirmed my impression that I was moving out of one realm of learning into another.

My work with Werner Erhard, to whose activities Tina Packer introduced me (screaming and kicking) in 1975, involved several of these changes, especially my new relationships with friends and family and my becoming a teacher. Erhard's work deserves a lengthier appreciation than I can give it here. Leaving out its more substantial aspects, I can say that from the start it appealed to me as the wittiest, most intellectually sophisticated example of social drama created in our versatile age (perhaps the instigators of the May 1968 events in Paris came close, in a quite different arena); and that Erhard and those he trained supplied me with so appealing a model for teaching that when in the spring of 1978, at the invitation of Georges Guy, I was invited to teach French literature at Bennington College, I was able to begin a new career.

I approached teaching with contradictory feelings. The work attracted me because I was eager to share with others the knowledge I had accumulated over many years of writing and reading. On the other hand, I was appalled by my lack of training in the disciplines of intellectual synthesis that I considered indispensable to a decent academic presentation of that knowledge. Werner Erhard's teaching method was anything but decent. He taught Heidegger and Wittgenstein in the language of a drill sergeant. He stripped philosophy (and culture in general) of its forbidding and also reassuring pretensions and made it relevant, even linguistically, to the concerns of the present moment. This method demanded great attentiveness and a willingness to take risks — challenging qualities, no doubt, but ones that to me still seemed more attainable than academic authority.

When I at last made the plunge, I found myself swimming in a new sea of discovery; and since the sense of discovery is what best holds the interests of students, the venture was not the failure I had so long dreaded and postponed. The guarantee of not failing, I later concluded, lay essentially in the promise I repeatedly made to myself always to be sure I learned more in a given class than anyone else in the room. My satisfactions, however, surpassed the new education I received. I discovered the unsuspected joy of working with others, with my students most conspicuously, but also with my colleagues, several of whom immediately became my friends, and whom I shall count as friends until the end of our lives: Georges Guy, Reinhardt Mayer, Nicholas Delbanco, Phebe Chao, Stephen Sandy, Leroy Logan, Vivian Fine, John Lydenberg, Martin Horwitz — a cluster of people so brilliant, kind, and loyal it seems nothing less than miraculous to have found them gathered in a little college in southern Vermont in the space of three years.

I believe that it was soon after my first semester at Bennington that I started work on *Cigarettes*. A year later, in the autumn of 1979, I began another process of discovery: a much admired (if not intimate) friend in Paris died of cancer. At the beginning of the new year two other men who were close to me died, and at the end of March my father suffered a grievous heart attack which he survived for only a week. I spent all but one day of that week with my father and mother, experiencing intervals (and no space of time was not an interval) of grief, fear, hope, and reassurance that I plumbed with (to me) bewildering clarity. The most bewildering interval of all was the fearful one. I found myself driving along the shore towards Southampton Hospital, certain that my father was dying there, with my teeth chattering and my hands firm on the wheel only by dint of desperate pressure (reinforced by the presence of my mother in the "death seat" next to me). I quickly identified my fear: I saw that, even if I had in recent years come to the warmest and most confident of understandings with my father, he was still a conveniently available enemy; that, once he was lost to me, I would have to find other enemies to take his place — something (someone) that I looked hopelessly for in the darkness that extended over the Atlantic to the distant left of the car I was hurriedly driving through the midnight March darkness.

Two Marches later I discovered something else about my father's death: that I had been able to endure it so faithfully, so clearly, so comprehensively because I knew that in my life I had the friend of friends, a second father who was also the older brother I had never had, and the younger brother, too, since (even if my ready deference to him suggested otherwise) he was my junior by six years: Georges Perec.

In the fall of 1981 Georges was invited to Australia, where in his letters he first mentioned a nagging pain in his hip. On his return to Europe, he went on a lecture tour through Italy, where the pain became worse. In November, back in

Paris, he consulted doctors fleetingly, tried different painkillers, saw an acupuncturist, who didn't help either, until a friend made him take tests that showed he had lung cancer.

In the light of such a revelation, it should have been obvious to the most indifferent observer that the pain in the hip was a metastasis of the cancer; but I wasn't indifferent. I could not bear any such obvious explanation. I took my leave of Georges while he was still determined to fight his illness with every resource he could summon. That was in mid January 1982; I was on my way to New York and Columbia. I spoke to him by phone a month later. In the beginning of March, on a date that I do not remember and that I haven't the courage to look up, he died in a hospital outside Paris, among others who loved him, spared the last gasping failure of his lungs by a timely administration of morphine.

After Georges's death I might well have fallen back into a convenient and familiar syndrome of isolation and abandonment if it had not been for Marie's presence, and if the "wake" of his death had not cast up on my needy passage two incorruptibly determined friends. The first was Joseph McElroy, who had for mysterious reasons come to live in Paris appropriately at the very moment Georges's illness was first manifesting itself. Joe was not like Georges, except in two things: he was confident of his genius as a creator of fiction, and he was committed to the celebration of present possibilities. We became friends without even trying, but I can scarcely scrutinise my own impulses at the time we came to know each other. It was as though I had been crying out for help when I did not have the least awareness that help was needed. Joe responded to that silent cry, and in the ensuing blinded months became a rock.

My second new friend showed up a year later, thanks to the recommendation of Werner Erhard. In the course of a seminar that I taught in San Francisco, I had lunch with Elizabeth Cowan, later to become Elizabeth Neeld. At the time she was best known for an extraordinary book on writing that she had co-authored with her late husband. We would have become friends whatever the circumstances; that we had each experienced painful loss only made our sympathy more immediate, and made it on my part a source of undying gratitude. Elizabeth had explored the consequences of death in a way that I was incapable of, or in any case unwilling to follow. She gave me clues as to how to move on, as to how to move out; she made available to me the lessons she had learned without ever suggesting that I believe them. She gave me the opportunity to give up grief for a new world from which grief need not be excluded. Since then, like Tina Packer, like Marie Chaix, she has been someone to whom I turn when events are more than I can handle alone, and who, with a reliability that never fails to amaze me, decisively demonstrates that I can indeed handle them alone, because nobody else is going to do it for me.

In the spring of 1985, in another March, David Kalstone was hospitalised with pneumonia. Its cause was diagnosed as AIDS. David began a fearful process of accepting and combating and being terrified (he kept that to himself). He lived another fourteen months, during which he returned a last time to his beloved Venice, where Marie and I spent a happy fortnight with him in early summer.

Later that summer, the summer of 1985, my mother began complaining of recurrent pains in her lower back. I told her that, on the eve of her eighty-second birthday, she should consider herself lucky that in a society decimated by aching backs she should have been spared this long. She was worried, but she put off serious examination of her trouble so as to be able to make one more September trip to Italy with Marie and me. She had hardly ever been sick; she was a woman of hearty appetites. In Italy her appetites failed her, she felt less and less well. On her return to New York, tests revealed an inoperable, untreatable cancer of the colon. Cancer was thus revealed, except to her: Mary Mathews, more herself than ever, carefully and stubbornly refused to recognise what was happening to her. At first I thought that she was wrong in this, that she would find her well-being in acknowledging the truth, in coming to terms with it, in accepting her end with some kind of serenity that was entirely my concern and not hers. What she did was exactly what she should have done, although I regret that I shall never know exactly how she interpreted the words "malignant tumour" — whatever the interpretation, she found a place for the words spacious enough to let her live with them, and with the tumours too, for many more months than she was supposed to.

During that time, I commuted transatlantically every month to stay with her. I was an only child, she was her father's only child, and I no longer knew who the child in question might be. She had a nurse, a housekeeper, and me. Every evening we spent together she would tell me stories of her past that I had never heard before, and she told me the stories with an exquisite clarity that laid before me the splendid hopes and disappointments (and the gossip, too) of her intensely lived younger years. On the first of July 1986, two weeks after David Kalstone, at the end of a death agony that lasted eight days and confounded the predictions of doctors and nurses, she died, having lived her life out to the last unjustified, pressureless heartbeat. As long as her heart kept beating, she remained my eternal shelter, so that I told myself, in some unspoken part of my being, that she could go on dying until the end of time, until the end of my time anyway, and I would still be protected by her. Such matters may be incomprehensible to those who have not experienced them.

In time the shelter I had lost dissolved into a stuporous haze. One afternoon, walking up Madison Avenue, I looked up, looked around. The haze had withdrawn. I saw my new shelter, now no lower than the sky itself. I looked in astonishment at the messengers, businessmen, businesswomen, shoppers, idlers on the sidewalk where I was standing. If they noticed me, they must have thought there was a crazy man in their midst, such was the love with which I stared at them.

1987

Related titles from Atlas Press

Claude BERGE, Italo CALVINO, Paul FOURNEL, Jacques JOUET, Harry MATHEWS, Raymond QUENEAU. *Oulipo Laboratory*, with manifestos by François LeLionnais, translated by Harry Mathews and Iain White, *Anti-Classics 4*, 176 pp, ISBN 0 947757 89 9.

The Oulipo has been publishing its own Bibliothèque oulipienne *for 25 years. This book collects together six complete issues which together cover a wide range of their activities.*

"An essential book for both newcomers and longtime students of this ingenious school of writers."—Review of Contemporary Fiction.　　　　UK £7.99, USA $15.99

Harry MATHEWS & Alastair BROTCHIE [eds.], *Oulipo Compendium*, introductions by Jacques Roubaud, Paul Gayot & Thieri Foulc, *Atlas Arkhive 6*, 336 pp, ISBN 0 947757 96 I.

A massive encyclopaedic exploration of the processes and concerns of the Oulipo group of writers, with sections devoted to their sister groups the Oupeinpo (painting), Oulipopo (detective fiction), Oubapo (comic strips) etc.

"Oulipo was — is — a seedbed, a grimace, a carnival. This is an indispensable book for everyone who cares about literature." —Susan Sontag

"Oulipo Compendium is a late 20th-century kabala, a labyrinth of literary secrets that will lure the uninitiated into rethinking everything they know about books and writing. The editors have done an astounding job putting together this nutty, one-of-a-kind book. It is the definitive encyclopaedia of contemporary word-magic." —Paul Auster

UK £16.99, USA $19.99